✻ abc
RAILWAY
QUIZ BOOK
Now & Then

Ian Allan
PUBLISHING

Contents

abc Railway Quiz Book Now and Then

First published 2015

ISBN 978 0 7110 3832 5

Published by Ian Allan Publishing

an imprint of Ian Allan Publishing Ltd, Addlestone, Surrey KT15 2SF.
Printed in Wales.

Visit the Ian Allan Publishing website at www.ianallanpublishing.com

Introduction

This *abc Railway Quiz Book* is an entertaining yet challenging test of railway knowledge for all railway enthusiasts, young and old. It comprises a comprehensive set of railway quiz questions with the questions arranged thematically in sections. Questions range across the entire history of railways up to the present day, and the book includes sections on locomotives and rolling stock, railway companies, personalities, signalling, infrastructure, railways and the arts, narrow gauge and miniature railways, modelling as well as many other subjects. Whatever your specialist interest, there should be something to intrigue and challenge you.

As an interesting comparison with yesteryear, the *abc Railway Quiz Book* from 1960 has also been included in the second part of the book.

This mine of fascinating facts, information and trivia will challenge even the most ardent of railway experts.

Introduction from abc Railway Quiz Book 1960

We have compiled this illustrated quiz book in response to many requests. The 275 questions cover all aspects of railways, from motive power and rolling stock to signalling, permanent way and general knowledge and history. It will be found just the thing for those moments during spotting expeditions when nothing is signalled through the junction, for the journey home after the day's shed outing, or to round off the club meeting. Although the book is intended mainly for the junior spotter, many an older student of railways will find plenty in it to rack his brains also.

The questions will be found in the first part of the book with the answers in the second part. There is no set standard of ease or hardness of individual questions, as it depends on your knowledge of particular topics of railway working, but they range widely from simple questions on locomotive classes for younger spotters to semi-technical questions for the older enthusiast. At the end of the questions is a pictorial quiz to test your powers of observation.

abc Railway Quiz Now – Questions

Signalling (Answers on page 39)

1. The initials MAS refer to Multiple Aspect (colour-light) Signalling. In an MAS signalled area what does a flashing single amber/flashing double amber signal mean to the driver of an approaching train?

2. In a mechanically signalled area, what does a white diamond on a signal post indicate to the driver?

3. In terms of signalling indications, what is a 'wrong side failure'?

4. In mechanical signalling, what is meant by the 'clearing point'?

5. In the days of mechanical signalling on the GWR what colour was the lever in the signal box which controlled a red-painted distant signal arm (generally pre-1927)?

6. In the days before bracket signals became commonplace, signals for diverging routes at junctions would all be mounted on the same post. In an example having two stop signals one above the other at a junction, how would the driver know which signal referred to the line diverging to the right?

7. Sometimes a single-arm stop signal might apply to several routes, any one of which would be indicated by a stencil appearing against a white background. What was the common name for this type of signal?

8. On a four-aspect colour-light signal, counting from the top, where is the green lens?

9. What was the purpose of flashing green signals installed on the East Coast main line north of Peterborough?

10. Until about 1970 there was an experimental indication in the form of 'yellow over green' at Mirfield in a four-aspect MAS area. What did this indication mean?

11. When a four-aspect colour-light signal is showing double yellow what does it mean?

12. What are ground signals used for?

13. Name the three types of fixed signals.

14. What was the initial cause of the multiple collision of trains at Harrow
   & Wealdstone station in October 1952.

Bridges and Viaducts (Answers on page 39)

1. On some viaducts, especially near stations, railings might be provided on
   top of the brickwork. Why?

2. In what decade were the last of the timber viaducts in Devon/Cornwall
   replaced by masonry?

3. At the time of the collapse of the first Tay Bridge in 1879, the designer
   Sir Thomas Bouch was working on plans for an even larger structure
   to cross what?

4. How many tons of steel were used in the construction of the Forth
   railway bridge when opened in 1890?

5. What was the name of the concrete viaduct on the LSWR Lyme Regis
   branch?

6. Crumlin viaduct in South Wales was the tallest railway viaduct in the
   UK. What was its height?

7. What is the name of the viaduct on the West Highland line reported as
   being the first such structure to be built of mass concrete?

8. In what year was the accident which caused two spans of the Severn
   railway bridge to collapse after it was struck by a barge?

9. The Kingsferry bridge is a UK lifting bridge for rail and road traffic.
   Which island does it connect to the mainland?

10. Brackley viaduct was a 255yd viaduct (now demolished) on which
   closed line?

11. Name the last of Brunel's timber viaducts to be replaced and when.

12. Which railway when first built in 1836 ran entirely on a viaduct, and
   how long was it?

Historical Railways (Answers on page 40)

1. A 'Brighton Terrier' locomotive was exhibited at a European city in the
   19th century – where and when?

2. A Gresley 'P2' 2-8-2 locomotive was tested overseas in 1934. Which engine and where?

3. Apart from the South Devon Railway, which other line in England used the atmospheric system of propulsion when first opened?

4. Which of the 'Big Four' railway companies had tentacles reaching into England, Wales and Scotland?

5. What was affectionately known as the 'Last Main Line'?

6. What were the two constituent companies that amalgamated to form the Midland & South Western Junction Railway?

7. What emblem was depicted in the centre of the crest of the Barry Railway Company?

8. In term of route miles, approximately how long (± 10) were the lines controlled by the Cheshire Lines Committee?

9. The Didcot, Newbury & Southampton railway was intended to link Didcot with Southampton by an independent route; however, it would fail to reach Southampton. What would be destined to be the location of the most southerly station on this line?

10. The Railway Air Service was formed in 1934 and used Croydon as its main operating and maintenance base for the pre- and post-war period. During World War 2 this operating base was changed – to where?

11. Which was the first public railway in Britain to be authorised by an Act of Parliament and when?

12. In which year was it declared that all passenger trains should be fitted with a continuous braking system?

13. Name the last major line to be built by traditional pick-and-shovel methods?

14. Name the first public railway in Wales, and when was it incorporated?

15. Name the Government organisation formed in 1914 to control Britain's railways?

16. Name the first railway to carry fare-paying passengers in trains hauled by a steam locomotive.

17. Give the weight in working order of *Locomotion* which pulled the first

train on the Stockton & Darlington Railway.

18. How many steam locomotives were working on BR in December 1958?

Personalities (Answers on page 41)

1. Who succeeded Dr Richard Beeching as Chairman of the British Railways Board in 1963 and held office for two years?

2. Henry George Ivatt was the son of Henry Ivatt of GNR fame. The exploits of H. G. Ivatt as the last Chief Mechanical Engineer of the LMS are well known, but prior to this with which other railway companies in the UK did he hold office?

3. In which country was Oliver Bulleid of GNR, LNER, SR and CIE fame born?

4. Who was General Manager of the Southern Railway during World War 2?

5. Several members of the Southern 'Battle of Britain' class carried names of particular individuals. With one exception, all had their official namings performed by the individual concerned – who was the exception?

6. What was the name of the artist renowned for his railway (and other) paintings who always included a mouse on his canvas?

7. After whom was the LMR 2-10-0 *Gordon* named?

8. What relation was Robert Billinton to Lawson Billinton, both of whom held the post of Locomotive Engineer on the London, Brighton & South Coast Railway?

9. What was the name of the younger brother of Dugald Drummond who held office on the Highland Railway and then the Glasgow & South Western Railway?

10. Who was General Manager of the GWR from 1921 to 1929?

11. Who was Capt Bill Smith RNR?

12. Name the compiler of railway guides and timetables who died in 1853?

13. Who designed the first British 'Baltic' type locomotive and for which railway?

Stations (Answers on page 41)

1. The Southern Railway produced many concrete structures used throughout the system from its concrete works at Exmouth Junction, but where was the equivalent concrete works of the GWR?

2. What was the nickname for the (mainly GWR) corrugated-iron huts often used on wayside halts whose shape was distinctly oriental in style?

3. Which London terminus had a 'lawn' with no grass?

4. From where in London did the British Rail 'Motorail' service operate between 1966 and 1995?

5. From 1948 until the mid-1960s, when corporate blue and its associate black/white lettering became the norm, the various regions of BR might be identified by specific colours. Often these were similar to earlier pre-nationalisation colours, but can you name all the post-1948 shades and connect these to the correct region?

6. In 2014, which station in the UK had the longest platform?

7. There are two main locations in Devon where it was once possible to depart for London in different directions, dependent upon which company's route was being taken. Where were/are they?

8. Victoria station in London was used as a terminus by which companies in 1922?

9. Under British Railways, Bath had two stations. Bath Green Park was on the Somerset & Dorset route; what was the name given to the Bath station on the Western Region main line?

10. What was unusual about how engines were removed from the front of their trains at Birmingham Moor Street station?

11. On what line would you find a station called Bungalow?

12. Name Britain's busiest station and give the approximate number of passengers who used it in 2013-14.

Permanent Way (Answers on page 42)

1. What is meant by the term 'switched diamond'?

2. Interlaced (or gauntleted) track is generally uncommon in the UK. There was however one fixed feature where this type of track was once

commonplace; what was this?

3. In England they are known as 'buffer stops'; what are they known as in the USA?

4. What is the general cause of 'rail-burn'?

5. The failure of a track-weld caused a major disaster on the Southern Region: where and when?

6. At which location was the Great Western sleeper works where sleepers would be 'pickled'?

7. What is the more popular name for a 'double compound' crossing?

8. For many years the GWR used a standard length of track panel that was somewhat shorter than the better-known 60ft length. How long was the Great Western variant?

9. Which railway company other than the GWR was a regular user of the term 'Economic Maintenance'?

10. What is the difference between a 'catch point' and a 'trap point'?

Openings and Closings (Answers on page 43)

1. From 1950 to 1962 inclusive (1962 being the year prior to Beeching), approximately how many route miles of railway were closed on mainland Britain: was it 1,000, 2,000, or 3,000 miles?

2. In what year did closure of the Midland & Great Northern Joint Railway take place?

3. The original Eurostar terminus at Waterloo opened in what year?

4. The original Tay Bridge opened in 1878 and collapsed in 1879. How long was it before the replacement bridge was opened to traffic?

5. In what year did the National Railway Museum open its doors at York?

6. Final closure of the last remnants of the Cromford & High Peak Railway occurred in what year?

7. In what year did the LSWR London station at Shepherds Bush close?

8. What was the first station in Britain to be given the suffix 'Parkway'?

9. In what year was the Serpell Report published, one option of which was the wholesale closure of the network leaving a rump of lines, mainly

those radiating from London?

10. In what year was the Severn Tunnel opened to trains?

Experimental Engines (Answers on page 43)

1. The Great Western was not known for its experimentation, preferring instead to rely upon conventional tried and trusted designs. However, one 'Saint' class locomotive was fitted with rotary-cam poppet valve gear. What was its name and number?

2. O. V. S. Bulleid used a 'test-bed' vehicle to ascertain the suitability (or otherwise) of sleeve-valves for use in his 'Leader' design. What was the name /number of this test-bed engine?

3. In 1961 British Railways trialled an 0-8-0 diesel shunting locomotive built by the Yorkshire Engine Company. It was never numbered but was instead known by the name it had been given by the manufacturer. What was this name?

4. Diesel Prototype No 2, more usually referred to as 'DP2', was the prototype by English Electric for what would subsequently become the Class 50 type locomotive. What, though, was Diesel Prototype No 1 and what, if anything, did it lead to?

5. What speed did the APT-E (gas turbine-powered) set reach between Swindon and Reading during a test run on 10 August 1975 in mph ±5?

6. Who was the designer of the first sleeve valve steam engine to run in the UK?

7. William Dean built two standard gauge 4-2-4T tank engines (only one, No 9, was fully completed); both were abject failures. In what form was No 9 subsequently rebuilt and then gave useful service?

8. One member of the 'Schools' class was given an experimental streamlined casing but never worked as such in traffic. What locomotive number was allocated to this experiment?

9. Which single LNER locomotive built in 1925 and scrapped in 1955 was temporarily converted to burn oil in the early 1950s?

10. Which company made the railcar fitted with both road and rail wheels that ran experimentally on the GWR and LMS in the 1930s?

Potpourri (Answers on page 43)

1. How many corridor tenders were built by each of the LMS, LNER, SR and GWR?

2. What 'badge of office' was typical of a station master at a large London terminus?

3. In 1968 a disastrous accident occurred at a new half-barrier level crossing – where?

4. What was the original wheel arrangement of the 'Fell' diesel-mechanical locomotive?

5. In 1926 the GWR purchased a four-wheel Sentinel geared steam locomotive. On which minor branch line did it work passenger trains for a short time?

6. What was the tractive effort of former 'Turbomotive' No 46202 *Princess Anne* after rebuilding as a conventional engine in 1952?

7. Which was the only class of express steam engine that operated on BR without a red buffer beam at the front?

8. In 1961/2 Euston station was rebuilt. What feature from the station was controversially demolished in the process?

9. You will have heard of 'Mansell' wheels – a composite wood and carriage wheel. But who was Mansell and where did he work?

10. Somersault signals were invented by McKenzie & Holland in direct consequence of the Abbots Rippon accident of 1876. Two railway companies in the UK were the principal users of this type of signal; which were they?

11. What disaster overcame the northbound 'Sunday Mail' train on the night of 28 December 1879?

12. What do the initials RETB stand for?

13. For what type of railway equipment was the Carlisle firm of Cowans & Sheldon best known?

14. The 'Docker's Umbrella' referred to which railway?

15. What event on the North London Railway in July 1864 frightened railway passengers?

16. How many steam locomotives went to Barry in the 1960s to be cut up

by Woodham Brothers?

17. What term is used to describe a train not fitted with a continuous brake?

18. What is the most serious danger to traffic on the line?

19. Which colour was adopted as standard for all BR diesel and electric locomotives in 1956?

20. Which brewer operated the most extensive brewery rail system in Burton-on-Trent?

21. How does an engineman traditionally brew his tea?

Sheds, Works and Depots (Answers on page 44)

1. Prior to the building of the large GWR steam depot at Old Oak Common in the early part of the 20th century, where was the GWR London steam shed?

2. After dieselisation of the Eastern Region main line, at what London depot were the 'Deltic' class engines maintained?

3. The Lancashire & Yorkshire Railway moved its locomotive works to Horwich in 1886; where was the original L&Y works located?

4. Where was the locomotive, carriage and wagon works for the former Midland & South Western Junction Railway located?

5. The 1949 film *Train of Events* had Jack Warner playing the part of an engine driver – the actor permanently injured his back when he fell into a turntable pit whilst making the film. At what London steam depot were the shed sequences filmed?

6. Before being located at Eastleigh, where were the principal locomotive workshops of the London & South Western Railway?

7. What was the name of the Highland Railway locomotive works at Inverness?

8. After 1923, where was the principal signal works of the Southern Railway?

9. Approximately how many engines were built at the former Stratford works of the Great Eastern Railway, ± 10%?

10. What is the name of the company that now builds railway vehicles at Derby?

11. Identify the three steam sheds in Carlisle operated by BR in 1960.

12. Which London shed serviced steam locomotives to work the 'Golden Arrow' service?

13. Name Britain's first diesel-only depot, and when did it become operational?

14. Identify the three steam sheds in Hull operated by BR in the 1960s.

15. What will the former Eurostar depot at North Pole be used for and when?

Railway Jobs (Answers on page 45)

1. Who said when being interviewed by James Naughtie in 1991 in consequence of severe weather causing travel disruption: '…we are having particular problems with the type of snow, which is rare in the UK' – subsequently corrupted to '...the wrong type of snow'.

2. What are the 'footnotes' that a signalman must be aware of before being considered competent to work a particular mechanical signal box?

3. What title given to the individual who would act as a 'human token' travelling on the engine, or authorise a driver to proceed over a section of line, where either temporary wrong-line working was in force or when there had been a failure of the single-line equipment?

4. Who was the engineer on the former Midland & Great Northern Railway who was responsible for the use of concrete used for signal posts and the like?

5. 'Charlie' was the name of the last railway horse working for British Railways until he retired in 1967. Where did he work? A clue might be that he was employed shunting horse boxes.

6. What was the title of the local permanent way man formerly in charge of a length of track?

7. On the GWR in 1923, who was more senior and why: the Chief Mechanical Engineer or the Chief Goods Manager?

8. What was the task of a Fogman?

9. Who was the famed individual in charge of the Isle of Wight railways for a period in the 1920s and 1930s? A clue might be that he was known

to countless enthusiasts as 'Uncle —'

10. What was the name given by the Southern Railway to a driver who only drove electric trains?

Rolling Stock (answers on page 46)

1. What type of vehicle was a 'Serpent' – the telegraphic code given by the GWR to one of its items of rolling stock?

2. Which railway company was the first to introduce Pullman carriages in Britain in 1874?

3. How many four-car double-deck units were introduced by the Southern Railway in 1949?

4. On which standard gauge railway in the UK were ordinary passengers permitted to travel in the brake van of goods trains on occasions?

5. Which two railway companies were the joint operators of vehicles carrying the designation 'West Coast Joint Stock'?

6. What was the colour scheme of the Tyneside electric stock of the LNER?

7. In BR days, brake vans were painted in either grey or bauxite – what was the difference between them?

8. After the LSWR decided not to continue operating sleeping cars what happened to these vehicles?

9. As is well known the GWR used telegraph codes to describe wagons: 'Mex', 'Toad', 'Pollen' etc. What may not be so well known is that it also had codes for passenger vehicles. Which one from this list is NOT a genuine GWR code: 'Gnat', 'Moth', 'Melon' or 'Snake'?

10. Mr Bulleid designed some Tavern Cars which operated under BR both on the Southern Region and where else on the network?

Railway Companies (Answers on page 46)

1. Which was the first of the five pre-Grouping Scottish railway companies (Caledonian, Glasgow & South Western, Great North of Scotland, Highland, and North British) to be incorporated?

2. Which railway company absorbed the 'Northern & Eastern Railway' in 1902?

3. In distance terms, what was the furthermost station from Waterloo on the LSWR?

4. What was the alternative name for the Hundred of Manhood & Selsey Tramway?

5. There are currently two operating stations with the name Bradford: 'Forster Square' and 'Interchange'. But which were the original owning companies of the now closed (1973) Bradford Exchange station?

6. Who is credited as having founded the Romney, Hythe & Dymchurch Railway in the 1920s?

7. It is 1922 and you are travelling from Norwich City to Melton Constable by the most direct route. On which company's metals would you complete most if not all of your journey?

8. Because there were two stations at Andoversford, one on the GWR and the other on the MSWJ, the names of the two were slightly different. That on the GWR route from Banbury to Cheltenham was plain 'Andoversford', but what was the full name of the MSWJ station?

9. How many railway companies existed on the Isle of Wight in 1922?

10. In 1923 the LMS and SR took over joint control/operation of the Somerset & Dorset route. Who had been the operators in the previous year?

Locomotive Names (Answers on page 47)

1. What was the original name carried by 'A4' No 4469, destroyed in an air raid at York in 1942 and by then carrying the name *Sir Ralph Wedgwood*?

2. Why was the SR 'Schools' class locomotive No 923 *Uppingham* renamed *Bradfield* soon after being introduced?

3. What was the number of the one member of the BR 'Britannia' class that never carried a name?

4. Which member of the 22-strong production fleet of 'Deltic' (Class 55) locomotives was the first to be withdrawn on 5 January 1980?

5. SR 'West Country' class No 21C125 was originally to have been named *Rough Tor*. What name did is subsequently carry?

6. Of the LNER 'V2' 'Green Arrow' class of 184 engines, how many carried names?

7. What is the collective class name for the Class 466 750V third-rail electric units?

8. Only ten BR Standard Class 6 'Clan' type engines were built. It had been intended to build a further 15, the names for which have been published several times. Can you give any <u>one</u> of these 15 projected names?

9. How was the name *Evening Star* chosen for No 92220, the last steam locomotive to be built for British Railways and completed at Swindon in 1960?

10. There were 30 members of the 'King' class built at Swindon between 1927 and 1930, excluding the replacement for No 6007 built at Swindon in 1936 using parts from the original No 6007 damaged in the Shrivenham collision. How many members of the class were renamed during their GWR/WR working life?

11. Why was 'Merchant Navy' class No 35019 *French Line CGT* unique?

Modern Diesel Types (Answers on page 47)

1. Which company built the Class 33 locomotives?

2. What fate befell diesel No 70012 as it was being unloaded at Newport Docks in December 2010?

3. What was the final total of Class 47 locomotives built?

4. In 1965 three pairs of Class 08 diesel shunter types were permanently coupled (with modifications to the cab of one unit and extra ballast weights added). They were known as 'master and slave' and also 'cow and calf' units. Where did they work?

5. Two classes of diesel locomotive have been given the BR 'TOPS' code 'Class 43'. One is the well-known 'HST' power car, but what is/was the other?

6. Excluding the North British D63xx and Swindon-built D95xx types, three main line diesel-hydraulic classes were based on the Western Region. Which of these never carried any names during its BR life?

7. What was the fate of HS4000 *Kestrel*, which worked on BR as a demonstrator between 1968 and 1971?

8. Most of the numerous Brush type 4 locomotives (later Class 47) were originally numbered in series from D1500 to D1999; however, the last 12 took numbers in a different series – what was it?

9. What was the BR Class 28 diesel?

10. How many main-line diesel-electric locomotives were operating on the Southern Region in 1954?

11. How many production 'Deltic' (later Class 55) locomotives are preserved?

12. How many wheels are there on a Co-Bo diesel?

13. In what year did the first main-line diesel locomotive run in Britain and when was it withdrawn?

14. Name the design consultant largely responsible for the external appearance of the Class 52 'Western' diesel-hydraulics?

Electric Traction (Answers on page 48)

1. What was the voltage of the original LBSCR overhead electrification scheme?

2. What makes the Class 92 electric locomotive type unique amongst straight-electric locomotives working in the UK?

3. Which electric locomotive was the solitary member of the BR TOPS Class 80?

4. Southern EMU sets have always been designated with a single digit (indicating the number of vehicles) followed by a 2/3 letter code (to describe the actual set). What does the designation '2NOL' signify?

5. The LNWR operated electric services including from Broad Street to Richmond, Euston to Watford, and Watford to Croxley Green. Where was the maintenance depot for the trains. If you are stuck, the answer is one of the given.

6. In what year did the first section of the LSWR third-rail network commence operation?

7. Southern third-rail electrification requires that there be a number of 'T.P.'

huts located at intervals. What do the initials 'T.P.' stand for?

8. What type of electrification was used for the Manchester-Sheffield-Wath route, known as the 'Woodhead' line?

9. In what year did Messrs Merz and McLellan produce a report on electrification of the GWR main line west of Taunton?

10. In March 1970 approval was given to electrify the WCML from Weaver Junction (where the Liverpool line diverges) north to Glasgow. When was this electrification completed?

11. How many electric locomotives did British Railways inherit when it came into being in 1948?

12. What was the standard supply for overhead electrification in the UK prior to the Modernisation Plan of 1955?

13. What was the power output of the Class 89 prototype ac electric locomotive introduced in 1986?

Speeds and Records (Answers on page 49)

1. What speed did the BR APT prototype reach on a test run in 1979, ± 5mph?

2. The BR 'HST 125' sets have a normal maximum operating speed of 125 mph. But what is their absolute maximum speed, ± 5mph?

3. In July 1938 *Mallard* broke the world speed record for steam. Which country had held the record before?

4. Which of the London Underground lines has trains which travel at the fastest speeds?

5. What was the maximum operational speed of the former Blue Pullman sets used by the LMR and WR?

6. What speed did *Rocket* reach during the Rainhill trials of 1829?

7. The BR Standard '9F' class locomotives were known for their turn of speed. Above which speed was an unreported member of the class once timed from Grantham to King's Cross?

8. What was the 'Race to the North' which took place over two summers in the latter part of the 19th century?

9. Whose design of streamlined railcar, which Nigel Gresley had observed

in France, was the inspiration for the famous wedge-shaped front end of the 'A4' class?

10. What is the top speed of the Class 395 'Javelin' electric sets when working over the third-rail network?

11. What top speed did BR's APT-P Class 370 achieve in December 1979 and where?

12. What then record speed did LNER 'A3' 4-6-2 No 2750 *Papyrus* attain in March 1935?

13. Name the only British 4-6-0 class of steam locomotive to have an '8P' power classification.

14. What was the largest and most powerful class of steam engine ever seen in Britain and where did it work?

15. Give the name of what was then the fastest British container freight train running in the 1960s.

Railway Books (Answers on page 49)

1. In what year were the first Ian Allan 'abc' books published?

2. David & Charles once had some former railway coaches outside its offices, at which station?

3. Approximately how many books is the late Oswald S. Nock credited with having penned , ± 5?

4. What is the name of the classic book by L. T. C. (Tom) Rolt on railway accidents?

5. To celebrate what in 1935 was *Railway Ribaldry* by W. Heath Robinson published?

6. Which railway author was awarded an MBE in 1993 for services to railway history?

7. Who were the four original founders of the Oxford Publishing Company?

8. Who set up Santona publications in 1994 and then moved to become the editor of *Railway Modeller* in 2008?

9. In what year did Kevin Robertson start his 'Southern Way' periodical?

Tickets (Answers on page 50)

1. Who is credited as having been the 'father' of the card-type railway ticket in use for over a century on Britain's railways?

2. On a card platform ticket, there was often a series of numbers '1-6' and '7-12' printed on the long edges of the ticket – for what purpose?

3. A ticket on which no starting or destination station was printed, leaving both to be filled in by hand, was known as what?

4. What was usually printed on the reverse of a card ticket?

5. What resulted when a card ticket was inserted into the small vertical press it was being issued?

6. What was signified by a red or green diamond on a card ticket?

7. When using card tickets, if a child ticket was not available what might the issuing office do before issuing an adult ticket for the same journey?

8. What was a 'Privilege Ticket'?

9. In BR days complimentary tickets of different colours were issued for first or second class travel. What colours were involved?

10. On the railway, what do the railway initials 'TTI' stand for?

Railway Nicknames (Answers on page 50)

1. What was the nickname given to *Mallard* as the holder of the world speed record for steam?

2. Why were the members of the SECR 'L' class referred to as 'Germans'?

3. In operational service, the GWR '47xx' class were never named nor it is believed did they ever attract a particular nickname. However, in connection with the project to recreate an example of the type, what nickname has been bestowed on the class in recent times?

4. So far as the LNER was concerned, what were 'The locomotives that won the war?'

5. J. G. Robinson designed the 0-8-4T engines inherited by the LNER and classified as GCR class '8H' and LNER class 'S1'; what was their nickname?

6. What in the 1950s was cruelly referred to as the 'Wonder' engine?

7. On what route does the 'Bed-Pan' service operate?

8. What was the nickname given to the first BR emblem used on steam engines and other vehicles from c1948 to 1957?

9. Which diesel locomotives were known as 'Bones'?

10. Who or what was known as the 'flying banana'?

11. What nicknames were given to the electric units built in the 1930s to work the Portsmouth line expresses?

12. What were nicknamed the 'Blue Trains' and when were they introduced?

The Great Western Railway/BR(W) (Answers on page 51)

1. The two Armstrong brothers, George and Joseph, were senior individuals at the GWR in charge of locomotives and rolling stock in the 19th century. Which brother was in charge at the Wolverhampton works between 1864 and 1897?

2. There exists a famous aerial image showing a number of 'King' class locomotives lined up outside Swindon shed in 1930. All the engines face forward. How many are in the line-up: 5, 6, 7, 8 or 9?

3. What was the name of the annual holiday outings involving special trains run from Swindon for workers and their families?

4. Where for the majority of the 20th century did the GWR have its famous 'clock shop' where station clocks and other timepieces were repaired?

5. What was the name of the former fireman/signalman who wrote four autobiographical books of his time on the footplate and in a signal box published by OPC from the 1970s onwards?

6. What were the nicknames given to the two different outside crank/inside cylinder 4-6-0 tender engines designs, both of which were 'one-offs' built at Swindon in the late 19th/early 20th century? Whilst neither design was perpetuated in its original form a modified version of one did emerge in quantity later as the 2-6-0 'Aberdare' type.

7. What was an 'Iron Mink'?

8. In 1935 the GWR introduced a new range of coaches having angular sides in a form of 'art-deco' styling. In many respects they were

similar to the 'Super Saloons'. What was the design of the general use vehicles called?

9. The very last ex-GWR pannier tank in industrial service remained in use until what year?

10. Who was Charles Spagnoletti?

11. What class was regarded as the ultimate development of GWR two-cylinder express locomotives?

12. In 1940 the GWR acquired two locomotives with the Weston, Clevedon & Portishead Railway. With what company had they originated?

13. From 1956 onwards what was the boiler pressure of the 'County' class reduced from and to?

14. Before the preservation era what was the last steam locomotive to work over the GW main line west of Plymouth?

The Southern Railway/BR(S) (Answers on page 52)

1. The Southern Railway had one flyover on its main line west of Salisbury – where was it?

2. In which renowned location close to the former LSWR main line is Dugald Drummond, the former Locomotive Superintendent of the LSWR, buried?

3. A popular speeded-up black and white film featuring a Southern line seen from the driver's cab and took just 4 minutes to travel from 'London to *where*?'

4. Which Colonel – operated several light railways in the Southern area as well as elsewhere?

5. Where was the main carriage works of the Southern Railway located?

6. At the Grouping in 1923, the former General Manager of the LSWR, Herbert Walker, was given the job of General Manager of the Southern Railway. What were the names of the General Managers of the former SECR and LBSCR?

7. What was the nickname of the meandering railway from Brockenhurst via Ringwood, Wimborne and Hamworthy, arriving eventually at Dorchester?

8. What was the traditional departure time from Waterloo for the 'Atlantic Coast Express'?

9. What type of steam rail vehicle was purchased in 1933 for use on the steeply graded Devil's Dyke branch?

10. On what former Southern line were the accident sequences in the film *The Wrecker* made?

11. How many express Pullman units were built for the Brighton line in 1932?

12. What was the final class of steam locomotive put into service by the SR?

13. In 1946 the SR added a former LSWR locomotive to its stock; what was it and from which railway had it come?

14. What was the boiler pressure of Bulleid's 'Leader' class?

15. From where did the Southern Railway obtain much of its ballast?

16. When built, the driving wheels on Merchant Navy No 21C18 *British India Line* differed from the rest of the class – how.

17. What colour were the driving wheels of No 34090 painted when the locomotive was named, and who was the locomotive named after?

18. How many Bulleid 'Light Pacifics' were rebuilt?

19. At what works was Bulleid Pacific No 34101 built?

20. The wheels used on Bulleid Pacifics and Class Q1 are different from other locomotive types; what is the nickname and how are they otherwise known?

21. Which SR locomotive was the most powerful class of 0-6-0 to operate in Britain, and how many were built?

22. Which class of SR locomotive was the last 4-4-0 type to be designed in Britain?

23. What nickname was given to the Drummond 'T9' class 4-4-0s built for the London & South Western Railway?

The London, Midland & Scottish Railway/BR(LM) (Answers on page 53)

1. The London & North Western Railway amalgamated with which other

large railway company just prior to the Grouping in 1923?

2. LMS No 6202, popularly known as the 'Turbomotive', was what type of turbine engine: condensing or non-condensing ?

3. Sir William Stanier was elected a fellow of which society, an accolade unique amongst his CME compatriots?

4. The highest point reached on a British standard gauge railway was 1,484ft at Wanlockhead close to Leadhills station on a line closed by the LMS in 1939. Which pre-Grouping company had originally operated this line?

5. What was the name of the main interior undercover circulating area at the old Euston station, now demolished?

6. What was the name of the LMS-operated railway company in Northern Ireland?

7. What is the name of the preserved 18in steam engine, one of eight that was used at Horwich works?

8. Four locomotive/carriage and wagon works were closed by the LMS in the years up to 1930. Name any of them.

9. In terms of route mileage, what was the furthermost station on the LMS from Euston?

10. Where on the former LMS was the national Locomotive Testing Station opened in 1948?

11. What was the class and number of the final LMS-designed steam locomotive put into service on BR?

12. What nickname was bestowed on the LMS 'Patriot' class locomotives when first introduced in 1933?

13. By what name were the ex-LMS Hughes/Fowler 2-6-0s generally known and why?

The London & North Eastern Railway/BR(E-NE) (Answers on page 53)

1. The route mileage of the LNER on formation was approximately what: 6,590 miles, 7,510 miles or 7,950 miles?

2. How many locomotives on the LNER after 1923 were fitted with a 'booster'?

3. What was the livery of most LNER carriages prior to nationalisation excluding special trains such as the 'Coronation' and 'Pullman' workings?

4. The Great Northern Railway used a particular type of semaphore signal that was neither of the upper nor lower quadrant type. What was it?

5. King's Cross locomotive depot was colloquially known by what name?

6. What was the livery of the LNER 'Coronation' train introduced in 1937?

7. What was the wheel arrangement of BR No 69999, formerly LNER 2395/9999?

8. In what year did the 'Selby diversion' south of York open?

9. What was the former name carried by the express passenger working latterly known as the 'Flying Scotsman'?

10. The LNER absorbed two docks operations from the former Great Central Company – where were they?

11. What was the class and number of the final LNER-designed steam locomotive put into service on BR?

12. In 1947 the LNER acquired how many 2-8-0 Austerity locomotives?

13. What was the original boiler pressure of the Gresley 'W1' class locomotive?

14. No 60010 carried a bell; who presented it?

15. How may Class A10 locomotives became part of BR stock?

16. Who designed the 'Decapod' locomotive for the Great Eastern Railway and how many driving wheels did it have?

17. Which class of Great Central Railway locomotives was nicknamed 'Fish engines' and why?

18. The Gresley 'K4' class locomotives were built specifically for working which line, and how many were constructed?

The Modern Railway (Answers on page 54)

1. Which company took over the operations of the former Knight Rail business at Eastleigh Works in 2012?

2. In which year was the Office of Rail Regulation established by statute?

3. Who was in charge of Scotrail, Network SouthEast and InterCity before later becoming Chief Executive of Virgin Rail Group for five years from 1999?

4. What is the maximum service speed of the Class 395 'Javelin' train-sets operating on 'HS1' from London to Kent?

5. Grand Central trains is a subsidiary of which other UK rail operator?

6. In what year did Network Rail commence operation, taking over from the former Railtrack company?

7. As at 2015, how many operators run passengers services from/to/through Reading station?

8. Approximately how many(±5) new stations have opened on the UK railway network since 2000?

9. As at 2015, what is the fastest journey time by train between Euston and Manchester Piccadilly?

10. Outside London, where in 2014 was Britain's busiest railway station?

11. Which is Britain's least-used station and how many passengers used it in 2013-14?

12. Identify the class of diesels employed to work Chiltern Railway's locomotive-hauled trains.

13. Name the three main rolling stock owners operating in the UK today (2015).

14. Which railfreight operator supplies the drivers and traction for the Caledonian sleeper franchise?

15. Which train operator currently runs the Greater Anglia franchise?

16. How many rail passenger journeys were made in Britain in 2013-14?

17. What is the current speed record for a train in Britain and when was it achieved?

18. How many Class 390 'Pendolinos' do Virgin Trains operate and where is the fleet maintained?

19. Name the company building the Class 700 trains for the Thameslink programme?

20. How many Hitachi-built Class 395 'Javelin' units were built for 'HS1' domestic services and when?

Model Railways (Answers on page 55)

1. What was the brand name of Tri-ang range of 3mm models?

2. The Kitmaster range included plastic kits for locomotives and carriages. So far as its OO range was concerned, how many kits of locomotives from the LMS and its constituents were produced?

3. New Cavendish published three high-quality books on the history of Tri-ang/Hornby covering the years 1950-1996. Who was the author of all three?

4. 'Peco' is the well-known trading name, but what is the company's full name?

5. What is the name of the background company that owns Bachmann?

6. Where in the UK does the Gauge O Guild regularly hold its major two-day show in September each year?

7. In what year did *Model Railway Journal* first appear?

8. *Hornby Magazine* is produced by Key Publishing. Who was the former owner/publisher of this magazine?

9. What do the initials 'DCC' stand for?

10. Which company now produces the former Airfix range of plastic lineside kits?

Welsh Narrow Gauge (Answers on page 55)

1. What was the name and gauge of the line that now runs alongside Llyn Padarn?

2. What was the gauge of the Pardarn Railway, and what were the names of its two termini?

3. *Blanche* and *Linda* have an older brother what is his name?

4. The Great Orme Tramway is cable-operated. What was the purpose of the original overhead line?

5. *Fire Queen* and *Jenny Lind* were built by which company?

6. How many narrow gauge locomotives did BR inherit from the GWR?

7. Talyllyn No 4 *Edward Thomas* was the first locomotive in the British Isles to be fitted with what?

8. Which narrow gauge locomotive had the distinction of working BR's last steam train when still in public ownership in 1988?

On the 15-inch (Answers on page 56)

1. *John Southland* worked on which line, and what is the locomotive's name now?

2. What are the names of the Bure Valley Railway termini?

3. 'Main Line in Miniature' generally refers to which line?

4. Which is the oldest 15in-gauge line still in operation?

5. A second-hand turntable was originally used at New Romney; from which line did it originate?

6. *The Bug* and *Black Prince* were built by German manufacturers – name them.

7. The Bure Valley Railway operates two half-size Indian locomotives; what are their wheel arrangement and class designation?

8. Which company manufactured the first steam locomotive to operate on the Ravenglass & Eskdale Railway, and what was its name?

9. Which line's northern terminus is at Etal Castle?

Miniature (Answers on page 56)

1. Wells-next-the-Sea has two miniature lines of what gauge?

2. What was the original gauge of the Fairbourne Railway?

3. What was the name given to a steam locomotive by HM The Queen in 2008, and on which line?

4. The Gorse Blossom Miniature Railway was in which county, and what was its gauge?

5. Which Scottish island once had a 10.25in-gauge line between castle and ferry?

6. Which 7.25in-gauge line has a location called Piggery Summit?

7. In what year did construction of the 7.25in-gauge Great Cockcrow Railway commence?

8. What was the gauge of the line that ran at Prestatyn?

Steam Engineering (Answers on page 56)

1. What is the purpose of a Gibson ring?

2. Where would you find a piston ring, and what is its purpose?

3. What are fusible plugs and where are they situated?

4. What is the purpose of a carriage-warming valve?

5. On outside-cylinder Great Western Railway locomotives how was the vacuum pump driven?

6. What are the six basic constituents of coal?

7. Where will you find roller bearings on some types of steam locomotive?

8. How many inches of vacuum were used in the braking system of GWR locomotives?

9. Which braking system was used on the Isle of Wight lines?

10. What was unique about the firehole doors on the Bulleid Pacifics as built?

11. What is the purpose of a 'jumper ring' on some Great Western locomotives?

12. What is the purpose of damper doors?

13. LMS Class 5 No 4767 (later 44767) is fitted with what type of valve gear?

14. In boiler design what is the name of the rod that connects the smokebox tubeplate to the backhead?

15. What connects locomotive Nos 34064 and 92250 – and what is the name of its designer?

16. What is the purpose of a 'slacker' pipe?

17. What is fed through a back-pressure valve?

18. Where would you find the big ends on a locomotive?

19. Name the locomotive engineers who developed the Kylchap double chimney?

English and Scottish Narrow Gauge (Answers on page 57)

1. Paper, pulp and diamond stacks are connected to which railway?

2. What is unique about *Unique*?

3. When the Ashover Light Railway was constructed, what were the only new items of rolling stock purchased?

4. Which line operated the locomotives named *Hampton*, *Kempton* and *Sunbury*?

5. In 1930 the British Film Institute produced 'A Quaint Little Line'. Which railway did it feature?

6. The Campbeltown & Machrihanish Railway shared a feature with the Talyllyn and Corris railways – what was it?

7. On what Scottish industrial line did *Dougal* work before preservation?

Heritage Railways (Answers on page 58)

1. Which heritage line takes its passengers for a ride 'Over the Alps'?

2. Which member of the Royal Family defected from Llangollen and arrived at the Mid-Hants Railway in 2015?

3. Which is the longest standard gauge heritage railway in England and how long is it?

4. What was the Heritage Railway Association's predecessor known as?

5. How long is the longest heritage railway in the UK and where is it?

6. Which railway now uses Swainsthorpe signalbox as a booking office, shop and waiting room?

7. *Bittern* marked the 75th anniversary of *Mallard*'s world record speed for a steam locomotive by setting the record for the fastest speed for a preserved steam locomotive on 5 December 2013. What top speed did it achieve on this run and where?

8. Over 200 locomotives were saved from scrapping at Woodham's scrapyard in Barry but only one ex-LNER locomotive. Which one?

9. A new-build LMS 'Patriot' is being built. What is its name, decided by public poll?

Names and Numbers (Answers on page 58)

1. What is the connection between Nos 2329 and 5529 (BR Nos 32329 and 45529)?

2. What is the number and name of the main-line locomotive 'sectioned' at the NRM?

3. In 1937 two LNER locomotives were rebuilt with streamlining; what were their numbers and names?

4. Why were some GWR 'Hall' class locomotives renumbered in the 39xx series?

5. In what way did the final eight of the Ashford-built 'N' class Moguls differ from the rest of the class?

6. Nos 92020 to 92029 differed from the rest of the BR '9Fs' in what way?

7. How many BR Standard steam locomotives were constructed, and in how many classes?

8. What were the numbers and names of the 'West Country' class locomotives to be scrapped by Woodham Brothers at Barry?

9. In an alphabetical listing of BR-operated steam locomotive names, excluding initials, which are the first and last?

10. What is the connection between 'A3' No 2563 (BR 60064) and 'A4' No 4462 (BR 60004) is?

11. What were the names of the highest-numbered Austerity 2-8-0 and the two highest-numbered 2-10-0s?

12. Why were the BR Sulzer diesel locomotives, introduced in 1959, called the 'Peak' class?

13. What was common to both 'Jubilee' class No 45641 and 'A3' class No 60039?

14. What was the name and number of the GWR's only Pacific locomotive?

15. Identify the two locomotives which were both named after King George VI?

16. What was the 'Zulu'?

Railways and Water (Answers on page 59)

1. Where were the first water troughs in the world installed?

2. What was unusual about Standedge Tunnels in the days of steam?

3. Which former railway-owned paddle steamer is still in service?

4. What and where was 'daddy long legs'?

Railways and War (Answers on page 59)

1. Why were some North British Railway Class C (LNER J36) locomotives named after World War 1 military leaders and places?

2. Which class of pre-nationalisation locomotive was built by all of the 'Big Four' companies, and why?

3. Who is credited as the designer of the Ministry of Supply (War Department) Austerity locomotives?

4. After the war, how many USA tanks did the Southern Railway acquire?

5. Name the military camp in Warwickshire built in 1940 with 3.5 miles of track and now used to store rolling stock.

6. What were 'Jellicoes' and where did they run to?

Multiple Units (Answers on page 59)

1. In 1981 LEV 2 was operational in which country?

2. The Long and the Short – what class could these designations belong to?

3. Where do the two Class 139s operate a captive service?

4. What did the single-car Class 153 start life as?

5. At what depot are the Class 159 units maintained?

6. The Class AM1 units saw operation on what line, and what were they?

7. In what year were the Southern Region Class 430 REP units introduced?

8. How many manufacturers supplied four-wheel railbuses to BR in the 1950s?

9. What was unusual about the Swindon-built Class 123, 124 and 126 Trailer First and Composite vehicles?

10. What class designation was given to the Blue Pullman units?

11. What were the Rolls Royce-engined Class 110 DMUs known as by enthusiasts?

12. Of the first generation diesel multiple units, Classes 113, 125 and 127 shared a common feature what was it?

13. The proposed Class 152 units were never built what were they to be?

14. Between which two principal locations do the Class 159s work?

15. On withdrawal from service in the UK a number of Class 141 units were exported where to?

16. Two prototype Class 151 units were introduced in 1985 and withdrawn in 1989. Who built them, and when were they scrapped?

17. When introduced, how many vehicles did the Class 253 and 254 consist of?

18. Name the units built specially for the new service linking Hull and Liverpool in the 1960s.

19. DMMUs are generally referred to as DMUs, but what does the additional M stand for?

20. What was the lowest class number allocated to DMMUs, and the highest?

21. Why were two Derby-built DMMUs rebuilt at Cowlairs Works in 1958?

22. In what way are the Class 325 units different from the rest of the '3xx' class series?

23. Upon closure of the Tyneside 750V system, what became of the bulk of the units?

24. On which line does the National Air Traffic Control operate a Wickham Railcar?

25. On what three Scottish routes were Swindon-built DMUs to be regularly seen?

Rolling Stock (Answers on page 60)

1. In the BR Standard series how many Griddle Cars were built?

2. What were the second-generation prototype coaches generally know as?

3. What does the abbreviation GUV stand for?

4. What does the abbreviation CCT stand for?

5. What is a Super GUV?

6. What is a Super BG?

7. What is a TCV?

8. What is a CARTIC?

9. Coach S1000S was unique amongst the BR Standard coaches – why?

10. Coach M2990 was unique amongst the BR Standard coaches – why?

11. The 1960-built Mark I Pullman Cars are in which number series?

12. The 1966-built Mark II Pullman Cars are in which number series?

13. What was the lowest running number of the Mark II coaches?

14. To where in 2008 did BR export a number of Mark II coaches?

15. What does the abbreviation RMB correctly stand for?

16. How many RMBs were modified to work with Southern Region EMUs?

17. RMBs in the 1801-1812 series had 48 seats, the remainder 44 – why?

18. How many Class 25s were converted for use as mobile generators to provide an electric train-heating supply?

19. In 1960/61 BR introduced two classes of Driving Motor Parcels Vans – what were they?

Isle of Man (Answers on page 61)

1. What line did *Sea Lion* and *Polar Bear* work on?

2. What was the gauge of the Douglas Southern Electric Tramway, and what date did it close?

3. What sets No 15 *Caledonia* apart from the remainder of the IoMSR fleet?

4. What is the only IoMSR locomotive to have been scrapped?

5. Where is No 3 *Pender* preserved?

6. On what part of the Island's network of railways and tramways is Groudle Viaduct?

7. What was the gauge of the railway on Ramsey Pier?

London Underground (Answers on page 62)

1. Until the line was rebuilt in 2007 what was unique about the track of the Waterloo & City Line?

2. What fate befell Class M7 No 672 at Waterloo on 13 April 1948?

3. At what depot are the Waterloo & City Line drivers based?

4. Which underground line has the longest railway tunnel in Britain, and how long is it?

5. Which artist designed the mosaic tiles at Tottenham Court Road Underground station?

Modern Traction (Answers on page 62)

1. What make of engines do the Class 70s carry?

2. The Southern Region Class 71s carried pantographs – why?

3. What class became known as 'Little EDs'?

4. Three companies built the Class 37s – which were they?

5. What was unusual about the braking of the EM1s as built?

6. How many EM2s were built, and how many carried TOPS numbers?

7. As built the Class 81s could operate from two overhead power voltages – what were they?

8. What was the number of the locomotive introduced as a prototype for thyristor traction technology?

9. Which locomotive builder has its works in Smethwick?

10. The Class 74s were rebuilt from which other class, and how many were so treated?

11. What does TDM stand for?

12. What engines did the Class 10 shunters have?

13. The Class 13 shunters were rebuilt from which other class, and what were they designed for?

14. The last operational Class 24 became a celebrity; what was its initial departmental number?

15. The Class 12s were Bulleid-designed; what braking system did they have?

16. What was the nickname given to the Class 33/2 series of locomotive?

17. What company built the four-wheel diesel-mechanical shunter No DS1169?

18. Where were the initial batch of Class 59s built?

19. What was the number range of the HST power cars as built?

20. The WR Class 42s and 43s carried warship names; which other class of WR diesels did so?

21. How many traction motors do the Class 08s have?

Railways in the Arts and Entertainment (Answers on page 63)

1. In 'The Adventure of the Bruce-Partington Plans' by Conan Doyle, near which Underground station was the body of the young clerk laid on the roof of a railway carriage?

2. In which cloakroom of which London terminus was a handbag containing Ernest found?

3. Which railway terminus in Paris was depicted by Monet in a series of paintings?

4. When William Powell Frith's painting 'The Railway Station' was first exhibited in 1862 it attracted thousands of paying viewers. Which station is depicted?

5. Which locomotive takes Richard Hannay on his escape from London to Scotland in Hitchcock's film *The 39 Steps*?

6. BR Standard Class 2 steam locomotive No 78018 is currently being restored by the Stainmore Railway Company. What is its claim to film fame from 1955?

7. The 2000 BBC TV series *The Railway Children* was filmed at which heritage railway?

8. In which famous poem does the poet describe watching newly married couples join the train during his journey from Hull to London?

9. What 1970s bestseller describes the author's journey by train from London, through Europe to the Middle East, India and Southeast Asia, returning by the Trans-Siberian Express?

10. What is the name of the fictional railway station in Kent at which Celia Johnson and Trevor Howard meet in the film *Brief Encounter*?

11. Identify the famous Victorian author who was involved in the derailment at Staplehurst in July 1865?

Railway Buildings and Infrastructure (Answers on page 63)

1. Who was of the architect who designed many new London Underground stations in the 1920s and 1930s?

2. Which building had two sculptures – named 'Night' and 'Day' – which scandalised the public when revealed in 1929, and what is the name of the sculptor?

3. What is the current name of Edinburgh's North British Hotel, which stands alongside Waverley station?

4. A number of signalboxes on the National Network are listed buildings. The most recent was opened in 1964. Where is it?

5. Which railway station in Yorkshire has Grade 1 listed status?

6. How many years did it take the build the Severn Tunnel and what was the cost?

7. How many tons of rail are being supplied for the Crossrail project?

Railway Geography (Answers on page 64)

1. How big was the British railway network at its height in the early decades of the 20th century?

2. Identify the most northerly junction on the BR system.

3. Where can you still find Devonshire Tunnel and when was it closed to trains?

4. How many level crossings are there in Britain today?

5. Identify the narrow gauge railway opened in May 1898 and closed in September 1935.

6. Where would you have found Strata Florida station and what could you have visited which was close by?

7. Which junction was reputed to be the busiest single-line junction during the BR steam era?

8. Where are Barry Links and Golf Street stations located?

9. Where in Scotland was the longest 'new' line since the 1900s opened in September 2015?

10. How did the proposed South Western & Isle of Wight Railway plan to

reach the island?

11. Where was The Mound located?

12. What was built and when on the site of the former LSWR power station at Durnsford Road?

13. Identify the three cities with stations named Queen Street prior to the Grouping in 1923.

14. Who or what were 'Port Road Paddies'?

15. Defiance Platform in Cornwall was opened in 1905 to serve what?

16. Where would you find Sugar Loaf Tunnel and Summit?

17. In which region of Britain did most rail journeys made in 2012-13 start or finish?

Identification

See images inside back cover.

Answers

Signalling

1. The train is due to be diverted over a crossover/on to another line, the divergence point for which carries a speed restriction less than the line on which he is currently travelling.

2. The section of line is track-circuited meaning the signalman will be aware of the presence of the standing/moving train.

3. A 'wrong side failure' is when a signal gives an incorrect indication, ie a green light when it should be showing red.

4. The 'clearing point' is a position, usually 440yd ahead of the stop signal at which a train is due to come to rest, which must be kept clear of any conflicting movements. Its purpose is to allow for an emergency 'over-run'.

5. Green.

6. Always 'top to bottom left to right', so the lower arm would refer to the right-hand line.

7. A 'route-indicator' or in slang terms a 'cash-register' signal.

8. It is positioned as the second lens from the top.

9. To indicate to the driver the route was suitable for 140mph running. Such use has since been discontinued.

10. It was a form of 'speed signalling' giving advance warning that the next signal was showing a double-yellow aspect.

11. It indicates a 'preliminary caution' with the next signal showing a single yellow.

12. Shunting movements within a station or good sidings.

13. Stop signal, distant signal and ground signal.

14. The driver of an express train over ran signals at danger.

Bridges and Viaducts

1. If the height of the parapet was similar to that of a platform, the purpose was to prevent a passenger opening a door in the belief that the train had arrived at the station and so stepping off into oblivion.

2. 1930s.

3. The Firth of Forth.

4. 51,000 tons of steel were used.

5. Cannington viaduct.

6. 200ft.

7. Glenfinnan viaduct.

8. 1960.

9. The Isle of Sheppey in Kent.

10. The Great Central Railway London Extension.

11. College Wood Viaduct on the Falmouth branch in 1934.

12. The London & Greenwich Railway with a 4-mile stretch over 878 brick arches.

Historical Railways

1. Paris – 1878.

2. *Cock o' the North* at Vitry-sur-Seine near Paris.

3. London & Croydon Railway.

4. The LMS.

5. The Great Central Railway London Extension.

6. The Swindon, Marlborough & Andover Railway, and the Swindon & Cheltenham Extension Railway. A third notional company later was the 'Marlborough & Grafton Railway'.

7. A Welsh dragon.

8. 143 miles.

9. Winchester – Chesil/Cheesehill.

10. Liverpool

11. The Surrey Iron Railway in 1801.

12. An Act of Parliament in 1889.

13. The Settle & Carlisle line opened in 1875.

14. The Taff Vale Railway in 1836.

15. The Railway Executive Committee in August 1914.

16. The Canterbury & Whitstable Railway in May 1830.

17. The engine and tender weighed 11.25 tons.

18. 16,108.

Personalities

1. Sir Stanley Raymond.

2. The London & North Western Railway and also the North Staffordshire
    Railway.

3. New Zealand.

4. Eustace Missenden – later Sir Eustace Missenden.

5. Winston Churchill.

6. Terence Cuneo.

7. General Charles Gordon of the Royal Engineers.

8. Father and son: Robert was the father and Lawson the son.

9. Peter Drummond.

10. Felix John Clewett Pole – Sir Felix from 1924.

11. The first person to buy a working steam locomotive from BR, and one
    of the founding fathers of UK rail preservation.

12. George Bradshaw.

13. Robert Harden Whitelegg for the London, Tilbury & Southend Railway.

Stations

1. Taunton.

2. Pagodas.

3. Paddington.

4. Kensington Olympia.

5. North Eastern Region (former GNR/GCR area) – Dark blue,
    North Eastern Region (former NER area) - Tangerine/orange,
    Scottish Region (north of the border) - Light blue,
    Midland Region - Maroon,

Southern Region - Green,
Western Region - Chocolate.

6. Colchester, at 2,034ft/620m.

7. Exeter St Davids and Plymouth North Road.

8. The LBSCR and the SECR. For a time prior to World War 1, the GWR also operated a few services from Victoria.

9. Bath Spa.

10. Due to restricted space, the station was equipped with two electrically operated traversers which allowed engines to move sideways. This was in place of conventional crossovers.

11. On the Snaefell Mountain Railway, Isle of Man.

12. Waterloo, with an estimated 98,442,742 passengers.

Permanent Way

1. This is where the actual elbows of the crossover move so as to present the wheel with an unbroken run.

2. At a weighbridge, where one set of rails was used if the vehicle needed to be weighed and the other acted as a 'by-pass' to the weighbridge.

3. Bumpers.

4. A spinning wheel, invariably that of a locomotive/power unit where grip has been lost. The resultant spin causes an intense build-up of localised heat.

5. Hither Green, 1967.

6. Hayes.

7. A double-slip.

8. 44ft 6in.

9. The LNER.

10. A catch point is installed to deliberately derail vehicles which are out of control on a gradient. A trap point is fitted to prevent unauthorised movement from sidings or branch line on to a running/main line. Either of these track fittings may lead the vehicles into a sand drag or safety siding.

Openings and Closings

1. 3,000 miles.

2. 1959.

3. 1994.

4. Eighteen years – in 1887.

5. 1975.

6. 1967.

7. 1916.

8. Bristol Parkway in 1971.

9. 1982.

10. 1886 to goods; passenger workings started on a different date but in the same year.

Experimental Engines

1. No 2935 *Caynham Court.*

2. No 2029/32039 *Hartland Point.*

3. *Taurus.*

4. DP1 was the prototype English Electric *Deltic* which led to the building of 22 members of the type used by the Eastern and North Eastern Regions of British Railways between 1961 and 1981.

5. 152.3mph.

6. Cecil Paget.

7. As a 2-2-2 tender engine.

8. Originally No 935 *Sevenoaks*, it was temporarily renumbered 999 for the experiment.

9. The solitary LNER 'U1' Garratt, BR No 69999.

10. Michelin.

Potpourri

1. LMS: 1, LNER: 22, SR: 0, GWR: 0.

2. A top hat.

3. Hixon.

4. 4-8-4.

5. Malmesbury branch.

6. 41,538lb at 85% bp. This was greater than the 40,290lb of the original 'Princess Royal' class and was due to a combination of having 'Princess Royal'-size driving wheels and 'Coronation- type cylinders. On paper this meant that at the time of its rebuilding, No 46202 was the most powerful express type operating on the LMR.

7. The 'A4'.

8. The Doric arch.

9. Richard Christopher Mansell was carriage superintendent of the South Eastern Railway at Ashford. Not to be confused with Richard Maunsell, the later SECR/SR CME.

10. The Great Northern and the Taff Vale.

11. The collapse of the Tay Bridge.

12. Radio Electronic Token Block.

13. Cranes.

14. Liverpool Overhead Railway.

15. The murder of Thomas Briggs by Franz Muller.

16. 297.

17. Loose-coupled.

18. An obstruction.

19. Standard Locomotive Green in April 1956.

20. Messrs Bass & Worthington with 16 miles of its own track.

21. In a white enamel tea can placed on the warming plate above the firehole door.

Sheds, Works and Depots

1. Westbourne Park.

2. Finsbury Park.

3. Miles Platting.

4. Cirencester.

5. Willesden.

6. Nine Elms.

7. Lochgorm.

8. Wimbledon.

9. 1,702 (+ 5,500 passenger vehicles).

10. Bombardier Tansportation.

11. 12A Kingmoor,12B Upperby and 12C Canal.

12. Stewarts Lane.

13. Devons Road depot in 1958.

14. 50B Dairycoates, Alexandra Dock and 50C Botanic Gardens.

15. To maintain the fleet of Hitachi IEP Class 800/801 trains to be introduced in 2017.

Railway Jobs

1. Terry Worrall, then BR's Director of Operations.

2. Local instructions applicable to the area controlled by that particular signal box.

3. The Pilotman.

4. William Marriott.

5. Newmarket.

6. The Ganger.

7. Surprisingly it was the Chief Goods Manager. It may well be argued that nothing could move without the products of the CME, but the Chief Goods Manager was considered senior as it was his department that brought in most of the revenue for the company.

8. To stand by a distant signal in conditions of fog or falling snow and place a detonator on the rails should the distant signal be displaying 'caution'. If the signal were cleared he would remove the detonator. A hut and brazier were provided as basic comforts.

9. A. B. MacLeod – also known as 'Uncle Mac'.

10. A Motorman.

Rolling Stock

1. A covered carriage truck.

2. The Midland Railway.

3. Two.

4. The Highland Railway – in remote areas where there was no convenient passenger train service.

5. The London & North Western Railway and the Caledonian Railway.

6. Blue and cream.

7. Grey signified a non-fitted (vacuum/air brake) vehicle, bauxite was used for a fitted brake van.

8. They were sold to the GWR.

9. The answer is 'Moth'. 'Gnat' was a slip coach, 'Melon' a brake third, and 'Snake' a passenger brake van. The 1939 GWR Telegraph Code Book also contained some other wonderful non-rolling-stock codes; 'Boyne', for example, meant 'There is no water at next station instruct drivers', and 'Earwig' meant 'Following urgently wanted'. Others included 'Stork', Chicory', 'Zola' and 'Smoke' – the last-named perhaps most easily understood as it referred to fog in the London area.

10. The Eastern Region.

Railway Companies

1. The North British in 1844.

2. The Great Eastern.

3. Padstow.

4. The West Sussex Railway

5. Lancashire & Yorkshire Railway and Great Northern Railway.

6. Captain J. E. P. Howey.

7. The Midland & Great Northern Joint.

9. Andoversford and Dowdeswell.

10. Four: The Isle of Wight Railway, The Isle of Wight Central Railway, The Freshwater Yarmouth & Newport Railway, and the New Ryde Pier & Railways – the latter LBSCR and LSWR joint.

11. The Midland and LSWR.

Locomotive Names

1. *Gadwall* – a common duck.

2. The headmaster of Uppingham school objected to the name of the school being carried on a steam engine.

3. No 70047.

4. No 55020, formerly D9020 *Nimbus.*

5. *Whimple.*

6. Seven – BR Nos 60800 *Green Arrow*; 60809 *The Snapper, The East Yorkshire Regiment, The Duke of York's Own*; 60835 *The Green Howard, Alexandra, Princess of Wales's Own Yorkshire Regiment*; 60847 *St Peter's School York A.D. 627*; 60860 *Durham School*; 60872 *King's Own Yorkshire Light Infantry*; 60873 *Coldstreamer.*

7. 'Networker',

8. 72010 *Hengist*, 72011 *Horsa*, 72012 *Canute*, 72013 *Wildfire*, 72014 *Firebrand*, 72015, *Clan Colquhoun*, 72016 *Clan Graham*, 72017 *Clan MacDougall*, 72018 *Clan MacLean*, 72019 *Clan Douglas*, 72020 *Clan Gordon*, 72021 *Clan Hamilton*, 72022 *Clan Kennedy*, 72023 *Clan Lindsay*, and 72024 *Clan Scott.*

9. As a result of a competition in the 1959/60 BR staff magazine.

10. Two: No 6029 was formerly *King Henry II* but became *King George VI*, and No 6030, formerly *King Stephen* became *King Edward VIII.*

11. It was the only BR steam engine which carried a name in upper and lower case and also in script style.

Modern Diesel Types

1. The Birmingham Railway Carriage & Wagon Co

2. The lifting-gear transferring the locomotive from the hold of the ship

failed and it dropped 13-20ft back into the hold. The damaged machine was subsequently returned to the makers in the USA.

3. 512

4. Tinsley marshalling yard.

5. The now defunct 'Warship' class.

6. The 'Hymek' type.

7. It was sold to Russia and shipped from Cardiff in 1971. After serving as a test-bed and basically 'reverse-engineered' the remains are thought to have been scrapped in 1993.

8. D1100 to D1111

9. The 'Metrovick' Co-Bo type.

10. The answer should be five: former LMS Nos 10000 and 10001 and SR Nos 10201, 10202 and 10203. However, readers may feel they wish to include No 10800 which was allocated to the Southern Region for much of the 1950s even if its reliability was such that it was out of service much of the time.

11. Six have been preserved.

12. Ten with one bogie with six wheels and the other with four.

13. No 10000 in 1947 and withdrawn in 1963.

14. Misha Black.

Electric Traction

1. 6,600V ac

2. They may pick up power either from the 25kV ac overhead or 750V dc third-rail system.

3. The converted WR former gas-turbine, E1000 later E2001.

4. two-coaches with no lavatory.

5. Croxley Green.

6. 1915 (25 October) – the Waterloo to Wimbledon via East Putney route.

7. A 'Traction Paralleling' hut.

8. 1,500V dc overhead.

9. 1939.

10. 6 May 1974

11. 17 from the former private companies.

12. 1,500V dc.

13. 6,000bhp.

Speeds and Records

1. 162.2 mph/261kph.

2. 148mph.

3. Germany in 1936 with a speed of 124.5mph/200.4 kph. Note: there have been claimed although unsubstantiated reports of *Mallard's* record having been broken in the USA both prior to and subsequent to 1938.

4. The Metropolitan line.

5. 90mph.

6. 29mph – note, it is reported as heaving reached 30mph in service the following year.

7. 90+ mph.

8. This was competition between companies as to which could reach Aberdeen the fastest travelling from London either via the West Coast or East Coast routes.

9. Bugatti.

10. 100mph

11. 162.2mph between Beattock and Lockerbie.

12. 108mph.

13. The ex-GWR 'King' class.

14. LNER Gresley Beyer-Garratt 'U1' class for banking work on the Worsborough Incline.

15. The 'Condor'.

Railway Books

1. 1942.

2. Newton Abbot.

3. 140.

4. *Red for Danger.*

5. The centenary of the Great Western Railway.

6. Colin G. Maggs.

7. Colin and June Judge, and Rex and Jane Kennedy.

8. Steve Flint – the Santona imprint was then taken over by Messrs Booklaw.

9. 2007.

Tickets

1. Thomas Edmondson.

2. This was so that the ticket could be clipped at a number corresponding to the hour it was used. Most platform tickets were for a single hour's duration and thus, when given up, the ticket collector would be able to identify if the holder had overstayed his allotted time.

3. A 'blank card' ticket.

4. A summary of the Rules and Regulations of the railway company to which the ticket and travel were subject.

5. The date of issue would be printed on the ticket; this was usually done on both ends.

6. It was a platform ticket.

7. The ticket might be cut corner to corner.

8. One that was issued often to a member of staff, for travel at a reduced rate.

9. Blue for second class and white for first class.

10. Travelling Ticket Inspector.

Railway Nicknames

1. *Mallard* has sometimes been rather unkindly referred to as 'the fastest duck in the world'.

2. Because 10 of the type were built by Messrs Borsig of Berlin – they were delivered in component form and assembled at Ashford.

3. The 'night-owls' – a result of the engines spending a fair proportion of their time working fitted freight trains during the night hours.

4. The 'V2' class.

5. The 'Wath Daisies'.

6. This was diesel No 10800, given the name by the operating department on the basis of 'I wonder if it will go today!'

7. Bedford to St Pancras.

8. The 'cycling lion'.

9. The Class 58, on account of its body shape having a narrow mid-section and a wide cab at each end.

10. This was the name given to the first design of GWR streamlined railcars and arose from on the shape of the vehicle. More recently the same term has been used to describe the Network Rail New Measurement Train but this time not because of the shape but because of its all-over yellow livery.

11. The units were known as 'Nelsons' or 'Pompey' stock.

12. Class 303 EMUs built in 1960 for the Glasgow area services.

The Great Western Railway/BR(W)

1. George Armstrong.

2. Seven.

3. 'Trip'.

4. It was located within the Reading Signal Works.

5. Harold Gasson.

6. The 4-6-0 'Crocodile' and 4-6-0 'Kruger' types.

7. Generally a four-wheel covered goods van having a metal body. Note there were also a few bogie 'Iron Minks' built.

8. 'Centenary' stock – so called as they were introduced 100 years after the formation of the GWR.

9. No 7754 was working at NCB Mountain Ash until 1975.

10. Spagnoletti was the first Telegraph Superintendent of the GWR and developed a number of signalling instruments, some of which remained in use until at least the late 1950s. His 'pegging' block instruments were often referred to as 'Spag blocks'.

11. 'County' class 4-6-0s.

12. London, Brighton & South Coast Railway.

13. From 280psi to 250psi.

14. No 34002 *Salisbury* on a rail tour.

The Southern Railway/BR(S)

1. At Axminster, for the Lyme Regis branch.

2. Brookwood Cemetery.

3. Brighton.

4. Colonel Holman F. Stephens.

5. Lancing.

6. Respectively, William Forbes and Percy Tempest.

7. 'Castleman's Corkscrew', so called due to its wandering course and its original promotor, Charles Castleman.

8. 11.00am.

9. A geared Sentinel was used on the line until 1936. After this it was tried elsewhere but was eventually withdrawn in 1940.

10. At Lasham on the Basingstoke & Alton Railway.

11. A total of 22 units.

12. 'Battle of Britain' class Pacific (No 21C170 *Manston).*

13. Adams Radial, East Kent Railway.

14. 280psi.

15. Meldon Quarry in Devon.

16. The were fabricated instead of cast

17. Malachite green with yellow rims; Sir Eustace Missenden.

18. 60.

19. Eastleigh, along with five others.

20. Boxpok, BFB – Bulleid Firth Brown – after the designer/manufacturers.

21. Bulleid Class Q1, 40.

22. The SR Maunsell 'Schools' class.

23. 'Greyhounds.'

The London, Midland & Scottish Railway/BR(LM)

1. The Lancashire & Yorkshire Railway.

2. Non-condensing.

3. Sir William Stanier was a Fellow of the Royal Society, hence the letters that appeared after his name on the nameplate of Pacific No 46256 *Sir William Stanier F.R.S.*

4. Caledonian Railway.

5. The Great Hall.

6. The Northern Counties Committee.

7. *Wren.*

8. Barrow-in-Furness, Maryport, Newton Heath and Stoke-on-Trent.

9. Lybster, on the now closed branch line from Wick – 742½ miles from Euston.

10. Rugby.

11. Ivatt Class 2MT 2-6-0, No 46527 in March 1953.

12. The 'Baby Scots'.

13. They were known as 'Crabs' because of their high footplate and the movement of the valve gear.

The London & North Eastern Railway/BR(E-NE)

1. 6,590 miles.

2. Four – a pair of what were originally GNR 4-4-2s of the 'C7' class and the two 'P1' type 2-8-2s.

3. Varnished teak.

4. The somersault signal.

5. Top shed.

6. Silver grey and garter blue.

7. This was the unique 2-8-0 + 0-8-2 Beyer-Garratt.

8. 1983.

9. The 'Special Scotch Express'.

10. Grimsby and Immingham.

11. Thompson Class B1, No 61399 in April 1952.

12. 200.

13. 450psi.

14. Presented by the Canadian Pacific Railway; the locomotive is named *Dominion of Canada*

15. One, No 60068 *Sir Visto*, rebuilt as an 'A3' in December 1948.

16. James Holden; the locomotive had a massive 0-10-0 wheel arrangement.

17. Robinson 'B5' class designed for working fast fish trains from Grimsby.

18. A class of five engines for working the West Highland Line.

The Modern Railway

1. Arlington Fleet Group.

2. 2004.

3. Chris Green.

4. 140mph/225kph.

5. Arriva UK Trains.

6. October 2002.

7. Three: First Great Western, South West trains and Cross Country.

8. 56.

9. 2hr 7min.

10. Birmingham New Street, No 8 in the top 30 busiest stations. New Street dealt with 34,748,000 arriving/departing passengers, although added to this should be a further 5,164,000 passengers who used the station as an interchange.

11. Teesside Airport with just eight recorded passengers!

12. Class 68.

13. Angel Trains, Eversholt Rail Group and Porterbrook.

14. GB Railfreight.

15. Abellio.

16. A total of 1.59 billion.

17. 208mph on 'HS1' in July 2003.

18. The 56-strong fleet is maintained at Manchester Longsight.

19. Siemens Transportation.

20. A fleet of 29 six-car units was introduced in 2009.

Model Railways

1. 'TT'.

2. Three: 'Coronation', 'L&Y Pug 0-4-0T' and 'Beyer-Garratt'. A 'Royal Scot' kit was also available but only in 3mm scale.

3. Pat Hammond.

4. The Pritchard Patent Product Company.

5. Kader hobbies.

6. The Telford International Centre.

7. 1985, although the idea was first discussed in 1984.

8. Ian Allan Publishing.

9. Digital Command and Control.

10. Dapol.

Welsh Narrow Gauge

1. Llanberis Lake Railway (Rheilffordd Llyn Padarn), 1ft 11½in (597mm)

2. 4ft gauge (1,219mm), Port Dinorwic and Gilfach Ddu.

3. *Charles*

4. It was used as a signalling system, today an induction-loop radio-control system.

5. Horlock & Co in 1848.

6. Seven (two Corris / two Welshpool & Llanfair / three Vale of Rheidol).

7. A Giesl ejector, from 1958-1969.

8: Vale of Rheidol 2-6-2T No 7 *Owain Glyndwr.*

On the 15-inch

1. Romney, Hythe & Dymchurch Railway, *J. B. Snell*

2. Aylsham and Wroxham.

3. Romney, Hythe & Dymchurch Railway

4. Rhyl Miniature Railway

5. Lynton & Barnstaple Railway

6. *The Bug* – Krauss; *Black Prince* – Krupp.

7. 2-6-2, Class ZB

8. Manning, Wardle in 1875, *Devon.* The first 15in-gauge locomotive was Bassett-Lowke *Sans Pareil* of 1912.

9. Heatherslaw Light Railway

Miniature

1. 10¼in (260mm)

2. 2ft, then 15in (381mm) and now 12.¼in

3. *Mariloo*, Exbury Miniature Railway

4. Devon, 7¼in

5. Isle of Mull

6. Great Cockcrow Railway

7. 1965

8. 10¼

Steam Engineering

1. It holds the tyre onto the wheel casting.

2. On a piston valve head, to maintain steam tightness between the piston and liner.

3. The plugs are screwed into the firebox crown, and if the water drops

below the top of the crown, the lead melts and allows steam to escape into the firebox acting as a warning to the enginemen, and extinguishes the fire.

4. It controls the pressure in the train-heating pipe.

5. By a driving arm from the crosshead.

6. Nitrogen, oxygen, carbon, ash, sulphur and hydrogen.

7. In the axleboxes.

8. 25

9. Westinghouse air brake.

10. They were power-operated, by the fireman pressing his foot on a pedal on the cab floor.

11. Its purpose is to alter the choke effect on the blastpipe and lessen the blast on the fire when the locomotive is working hard.

12. They are used to control primary air to the grate.

13. Stephenson link motion.

14. Longitudinal stay.

15. Both were fitted with Giesl ejectors, designed Dr Giesl-Gieslingen.

16. To damp down the coal dust on the footplate and bunker / tender.

17. Lubricant for the cylinders and axleboxes.

18. The large ends of a connecting rod.

19. Kylala and Chapelon.

English and Scottish Narrow Gauge

1. Sittingbourne & Kemsley Light Railway.

2. It is a narrow gauge fireless locomotive.

3. The four passenger coaches, even then the bogies were second hand.

4. Hampton & Kempton Waterworks Railway

5. Leek & Manifold Valley Light Railway

6. A gauge of 2ft 3in

7. Provan Gas Works Railway in Glasgow; today it is on the Welshpool & Llanfair Railway.

Heritage Railways

1. Mid-Hants Railway. Just to the east of Medstead & Four Marks, the line is the highest in Hampshire; the gradient from Ropley is 1 in 60.

2. An express bogie brake van, nicknamed 'Queen Mary', so named as they rode like an ocean liner.

3. West Somerset Railway at 22.75 miles (36.61km).

4. The Association of Independent Railway Preservation Societies, originally the Association of Railway Preservation Societies.

5. 25 miles (the Welsh Highland Railway).

6. Wells & Walsingham Railway.

7. 93mph on the 'Tyne Tees Streak' between York and Newcastle.

8. Class B1 No 61264.

9. *The Unknown Warrior*.

Names and Numbers

1. Both named *Stephenson*.

2. 35029 *Ellerman Lines*.

3. 2859 (BR 61659) *East Anglian* and 2870 (BR 61670) *City of London*.

4. They were renumbered when converted to oil firing.

5. Nos 1407-14 were built as left-hand drive, compared to right-hand drive for all the others.

6. They were built with Franco-Crosti boilers.

7. 999, 12 classes.

8. Nos 34045 *Ottery St Mary* and 34094 *Mortehoe*.

9. *Abberley Hall* (No 4981) and *Zeebrugge* (No 62666).

10. The 'A3' was called *William Whitelaw* until the name was transferred to the 'A4' in 1941.

11. 2-8-0 No 90732 *Vulcan*; 2-10-0 Nos 90773 and 90774 were both named *North British*.

12. Each locomotive carried the name of a British mountain or peak.

13. Both locomotives carried the name *Sandwich*.

14. No 111 *Great Bear*.

15. 'King' class No 6028 and 'Princess Coronation' class No 46244.

16. The name given to a GWR broad-gauge express to the West of England.

Railways and Water

1. Mochdre on the London & North Western Railway.

2. The tunnel was the only level stretch on the trans-Pennine route and incorporated water troughs

3. *Waverley*

4. The Brighton & Rottingdean Seashore Electric Railway that ran through the shallow coastal waters in Brighton between 1896 and 1901.

Railways and War

1. 25 of the class served overseas in 1917/18.

2. Stanier Class 8F 2-8-0s during World War 2 as part of the war effort for the Ministry of Supply.

3. Riddles.

4. 14 were taken into capital stock, and another survived at Eastleigh Works as a source of spares.

5. Long Marston.

6. The nickname for the special trains used to take HM Forces, and coal supplies, to Thurso for onward shipment to Scapa Flow.

Multiple Units

1. In the USA between Concord (New Hampshire) to Lowell (Massachusetts).

2. The Class 201 (Short) and Class 202 or 203 (Long) units used on the Hastings line service.

3. On the Stourbridge shuttle.

4. Two-car Class 155 units.

5. Salisbury.

6. The Lancaster-Morecambe/Heysham line, being prototype 25kV ac sets rebuilt from 1914 LNWR stock.

7. 1966.

8. Six: British United Traction (BUT), Bristol/Eastern Coach Works, Waggon & Maschinenbau, Wickham, Park Royal, AC Cars.

9. They had side corridors, unlike the Trailer Seconds that were of standard open configuration.

10. Class 251

11. Calder Valley, after the area in which they worked.

12. The were diesel-hydraulic units rather than the otherwise standard diesel-mechanical format.

13. Proposed rebuilds of two-car Class 156 units as single vehicles.

14. Waterloo and Exeter.

15. Iran.

16. Built by Metopolitan Cammell and scrapped in 2004 after several abortive attempts to refurbish them.

17. 882, 58 nine-car units, 36 ten-car units.

18. Class 124 'Trans-Pennine' DMUs.

19. Mechanical (as in Diesel Mechanical Multiple Unit).

20. Lowest 100, highest 190 (later reclassified as Class 126).

21. To trial battery-electric traction technology.

22. They were built for the Royal Mail postal traffic with no passenger carrying accommodation.

23. They were transferred to the Southern Region.

24. Snaefell Mountain Railway, to maintain the aerial masts at the top.

25. Edinburgh Waverley to Glasgow Queen Street, Aberdeen to Inverness, Glasgow St Enoch, and Glasgow Central to Ayr and Stranraer.

Rolling Stock

1. Six: Nos 1100-1102 (at Ashford/Eastleigh) and Nos 1103-1105 (at Doncaster).

2. XP64 stock.

3. General Utility Van.

4. Covered Carriage Truck.

5. A High Security Mail Van.

6. A High Security Brake Van.

7. A Two-Tier Car Transporter Van.

8. A Two-Tier Articulated Car Carrier.

9. It had a glass-reinforced plastic body.

10. It was designated a Discotheque, converted from SO 3735 in 1973, withdrawn 1976.

11. 311-354.

12. 500-586.

13. 1200.

14. New Zealand.

15. Open Second with Miniature Buffet, but generally referred to as Restaurant Miniature Buffet.

16. Two: Nos 1872 (in unit 2601) and 1873 (in unit 2602).

17. The later batches had a store cupboard in place of four seats and a table.

18. Three.

19. Classes 128 and 129; the Class 129 was introduced in 1958 while the other classes were rebuilt from passenger units.

Isle of Man

1. Groudle Glen Railway.

2. Standard gauge, closing during World War 1, reopening in 1919 and final closure was at the start of World War 2.

3. It's an 0-6-0T and built by Dübs & Co.

4. No 2 *Derby*.

5. At the Museum of Science & Industry, Manchester, as a sectioned exhibit.

6. Manx Electric Railway.

7. 3ft (914mm).

London Underground

1. The rails were vertical, instead of set at the usual 1 in 20 inclination.

2. It fell down the Armstrong lift that then gave access to the Waterloo & City Line. It was cut up in situ.

3. Leytonstone.

4. The Northern Line tunnel is 17.27 miles (27,800m [91,200ft]).

5. Sir Eduardo Paolozzi.

Modern Traction

1. General Electric/Jenbacher V16 GEJ616.

2. To collect traction power from overhead cabling in places where a third rail would be dangerous (eg freight yards).

3. Class 73.

4. English Electric, Vulcan Foundry, Robert Stephenson & Hawthorns.

5. They were fitted with regenerative braking.

6. Seven were built, and classified as Class 77 but never renumbered in this series.

7. 6.25kV and 25kV ac.

8. 87101.

9. Birmingham Railway Carriage & Wagon.

10. Class 71, 10.

11. Time Duplex Multiplexing.

12. Blackstone ER6.

13. Rebuilt from two Class 08s, designed for hump shunting at Tinsley marshalling yard.

14. 968007 (was BR No 24061).

15. Air on locomotive, vacuum on train.

16. 'Slim Jims', being narrow-bodied for working the Hastings line.

17. Bristol Aeroplane Co of Bristol in 1946.

18. La Grange, Illinois, USA, by General Motors.

19. 43002-43198.

20. Class 50.

21. Two.

Railways in the Arts and Entertainment

1. Gloucester Road.

2. Victoria Station, the Brighton Line (*The Importance of Being Earnest* by Oscar Wilde).

3. Gare Saint-Lazare.

4. Paddington.

5. LNER Class A3 No 2595 *Trigo*.

6. It was the stranded locomotive in the BTF film *Snowdrift at Bleath Gill.*

7. The Bluebell Railway.

8. 'Whitsun Weddings' by Philip Larkin.

9. *The Great Railway Bazaar* by Paul Theroux.

10. Milford Junction (the scenes were in fact filmed at Carnforth railway station).

11. Charles Dickens.

Railway Buildings and Infrastructure

1. Charles Holden.

2. 55 Broadway (London Transport headquarters). Jacob Epstein.

3. The Balmoral.

4. Birmingham New Street.

5. Huddersfield.

6. Thirteen years to build at a cost of almost £2 million.

7. 6,890 tons.

Railway Geography

1. c21,000 route miles, roughly twice its current size.

2. Georgemas.

3. South of Bath on the Somerset & Dorset line, closed in 1966 and now part of a cycleway.

4. Approximately 8,000.

5. The Lynton & Barnstaple Railway.

6. A station on the Carmarthen-Aberystwyth line that served the ruined Abbey.

7. Smallbrook Junction on the Isle of Wight.

8. On the line between Dundee and Carnoustie.

9. The Borders Railway between Shawfair and Tweedbank.

10. By means of a rail tunnel under the Solent between Lymington and Yarmouth.

11. It was the junction station for the Dornoch branch in Scotland.

12. Wimbledon depot inspection shed in 1976.

13. Cardiff, Exeter and Glasgow

14. The nickname for expresses that used to run to Stranraer via Dumfries.

15. The nearby Royal Navy torpedo training school.

16. On the Central Wales line between Llanwrtyd and Cynghordy.

17. London and the South East (62%).

Identification

A Welshpool & Llanfair Railway 0-6-0T

B BR Class 37

C LMS Class 5MT

D BR Class 20

E Alresford, Mid-Hants Railway

F Weybourne, North Norfolk Railway

G Blaenau Ffestiniog, Ffestiniog Railway

abc Railway Quiz Book 1960 - Questions

Locomotives (Answers on page 80)

1. What is a Compound locomotive and how does it work in comparison to a simple locomotive?

2. What is a superheated locomotive?

3. Which was the first 'Pacific' locomotive to run on a British railway?

4. What was the last design of 'Pacific' to be built for British Railways and where was it built?

5. How many cylinders has it and what form of valve gear does it use?

6. The WR 'County' class are now being rebuilt with double chimneys; which one has always had a double chimney?

7. Before modification the SR Bulleid Pacifics had a novel form of valve gear. What was it?

8. Which was the first 'Merchant Navy' class locomotive to be rebuilt?

9. For many years the Midland Railway and the LMS used a special locomotive for banking trains on the Lickey incline, near Birmingham; what wheel arrangement did it have?

10. What nickname did it have?

11. And what was its BR number?

12. What is a brick arch?

13. What is a petticoat pipe?

14. Many tank locomotives are fitted with condensing equipment, what is the purpose of this?

14. What is the main difference between a diesel-electric and a diesel-hydraulic locomotive?

16. Which region of British Railways has decided to adopt the diesel-hydraulic system for its main line locomotives?

17. When a locomotive is said to be 'priming' what condition is it in?

18. How many cylinders have the following?
    (a) 'Britannia' 4-6-2
    (b) 'Coronation' 4-6-2
    (c) 'King' 4-6-0

(d) 'County' 4-6-0

(e) 'West Country' 4-6-2

(f) 'Jubilee' 4-6-0

(g) 'Lord Nelson' 4-6-0

(h) 'A2' 4-6-2.

19. Who designed the LNER 'A4' class and when was it introduced?

20. The LNER also introduced a 4-6-4 locomotive, whose original number was 10000. What was its peculiarity?

21. It later became Class W1, what was its BR number and when was it withdrawn from service?

22. In Britain a 4-6-4 locomotive is called a 'Baltic'. What are the names given to the following?

(a) 4-4-2

(b) 2-6-0

(c) 4-6-2.

23. Why is Walschaerts valve gear so called?

24. What is tractive effort?

25. What is the 'big end?'

26. What is the most powerful 4-4-0 class running on British Railways? Who designed it and when did it appear?

27. What is a boiler ring?

28. Which British railway company ran a steam-turbine-driven 4-6-2 locomotive for many years and what was its number?

29. Two of the LNER 'Sandringham' 4-6-0s ran for some time fully streamlined—which two and why were they so treated?

30. What do the classifications 7P5F, 6P, 5F, etc signify?

31. What does RA1, RA2, RA3, etc., signify on an ER locomotive?

32. How can you tell the route availability of Western Region locomotives?

33. What was the first main-line diesel-electric locomotive to run on a British railway and where was it built and when?

34. What was the 'Fell' locomotive?

35. Which British railway company built the first 0-10-0 locomotive and what was it called?

36. What are Caprotti valves?

37. To which standard British Railways designs has Caprotti valve gear been applied?

38. What is the tractive effort of each of the following?

    (a) 'A4'

    (b) 'Duchess'

    (c) 'King Arthur'

    (d) 'Jubilee' (unrebuilt)

    (e) 'A1'

    (f) 'Castle'

    (g) 'Clan'

    (h) 'Hall'.

39. How many three-cylinder locomotives were owned by the GWR in 1947?

40. What was the 'Leader' class, and who designed it?

41. What are cylinder cocks, or drains?

42. What is a fusible plug?

43. What is the horse power of the following diesel locomotive designs?
(a) D1 class; (b) D8000 class; (c) D6100 class; (d) D800 class; (e) D5300 class; (f) D200 class; (g) D8200 class?

44. What was the first main-line diesel locomotive to appear in service under the Modernisation Plan for British Railways, and when did it enter service?

45. What is the horse power of the 'Deltic' locomotive and why is the locomotive so named?

46. How are the shed allocations of locomotives shown on them?

47. What is a capuchon?

48. WR gas turbine locomotive No 18100 was withdrawn from service and converted to what?

49. What wheel arrangement have the following types of diesel locomotives?
(a) D7; (b) D203; (c) Prototype 'Deltic'; (d) D601; (e) D809;
(f) D2222; (g) D2417; (h) D3333; (i) D5719; (j) D5909; (k) D6105;
(l) D6303; (m) D8035; (n) 10001; (o) D8409.

50. To which railways did the following locomotives originally belong?
    (a) *Locomotion*; (b) *North Star*; (c) *Coppernob*; (d) *Cornwall*;
    (e) *Gordon Highlander*; (f) *Boxhill*; (g) *Ben Alder*; (h) *Henry Oakley*;
    (i) *City of Truro*; (j) *Gladstone*.

51. What have all the above locomotives in common?

52. What is a taper boiler?

53. What is a hornblock?

54. What is the total weight of an LMR 'Royal Scot' without tender?

55. Which British railways used the Beyer-Garratt articulated type of locomotive?

56. Which classes of locomotives are referred to as 'air-smoothed'?

57. To which classes are the following nicknames often applied?
    (a) 'Black Five'; (b) 'Spamcan'; (c) 'Jinty'; (d) 'Greyhound';
    (e) 'Terrier'; (f) 'Dukedog'; (g) 'Mickey mouse'.

58. Which region does not equip the tenders of its locomotives with water scoops?

59. What is a 'light engine'?

60. What are balance weights?

61. What is the horse-power of the SR E5000 class Bo-Bo electric locomotives?

62. Which railway workshop built them?

63. Which famous sleeping car express is regulaly hauled by an E5000 type locomotive?

64. What is a service locomotive?

65. What is a guard iron?

66. What is a steam chest?

67. How many exhaust beats per one complete wheel revolution have three-cylinder and two-cylinder locomotives respectively?

68. What is the function of smoke deflectors?

69. What is the function of an axle box?

70. When an axle box is referred to as 'hot' what has occurred?

71. What are lamp-irons?

72. What is the smoke box saddle?

73. What is a pony truck?

74. What is a radial truck?

75. Which three standard Class 9F 2-10-0s are fitted with mechanical stokers?

76. What are tank vents?

77. What is the tallest class of British steam locomotive from rail to top of chimney?

78. No 60022 *Mallard* holds the world speed record for a steam locomotive. How many coaches was it hauling, where did it achieve the maximum speed, what was the speed, and on what date was the record run made?

79. What is a Belpaire firebox?

80. What is the ash pan?

81. Which design is the 'odd-man-out' amongst the following?
(a) the 'Hall' class; (b) the LMR Class 5; (c) the ER 'B1' class; (d) the SR 'West Country' class.

82. What, on the other hand, have they all in common?

83. Which is the 'odd-man-out' amongst the following and why?
(a) the 'A4' class; (b) the 'Coronation' class; (c) the 'Merchant Navy' class, and why?

84. When were the following designs introduced and who were the respective chief mechanical engineers responsible for introducing them?
(a) the 'King' class; (b) the 'A4' class; (c) the 'A3' class; (d) the 'Rebuilt Royal Scot' class; (e) the 'Merchant Navy' class; (f) the 'Princess Royal' class; (g) the 'Jubilee' class; (h) the 'Castle' class; (i) the 'West Country' class; (j) the 'V2' class; (k) the 'Lord Nelson' class.

85. What is a 'dead' engine?

86. What is a 'pilot' engine?

87. What was the highest speed attained by a locomotive of the LMSR, where was it attained, by which locomotive and when?

88. Which is the most powerful 0-6-0 design running on BR?

89. Who designed it; what is its tractive effort?

90. What is the number of the first 25kV ac electric locomotive to be introduced on British Railways as part of the modernisation plan and when was it delivered?

Spotters' Corner (Answers on page 85)

91. What is the number of *Lord Rodney* and what class is it?

92. What is the number of *Rodney* and what class is it?

93. What class is No 45551?

94. What tractive effort have the following?
    (a) WR '9400' class 0-6-0PT; (b) SR 'M7' 0-4-4T; (c) LMR Class 3F 'Jinty' 0-6-0T; (d) ER 'J50' 0-6-0T.

95. What are the names of the following?
    (a) 60111; (b) 46205; (c) 46133; (d) 30854; (e) 34006; (f) 61379;
    (g) 6015; (h) D809 (i) 46254; (j) D3; (k) 26000; (l) D602; (m) 60027;
    (n) 6900; (o) 70009; (p) 46101; (q) 60800; (r) 7007; (s) 35003;
    (t) 34090; (u) 72009; (v) 45536; (w) 30931 (x) 4082; (y) 60525;
    (z) 60157.

96. Which class of Pacifics has some tenders equipped with corridors?

97. Is an 'A3' Pacific classed as 8P or 7P?

98. How many LMS Stanier Class 5 4-6-0s were built?

99. Four Stanier Class 5 4-6-0s have names; which are they and what are the names?

100. Who designed the ER 'B1' class?

101. Where were the Standard Class 7 'Britannia' 4-6-2s designed?

102. And where were they built?

103. How many 'Princess Royal' class locomotives are there?

104. Which depots do the following shed codes denote?
     (a) 1B; (b) 64A; (c) 17A; (d) 84A; (e) 71B; (f) 89A; (g) 33C; (h) 32B;
     (i) 26A; (j) 51A; (k) 34B; (l) 9A; (m) 60A; (n) 75A; (o) 82C; (p) 66A.

105. Which BR locomotive depot was the first to be converted entirely to diesel traction?

106. To which classes do the following locomotives belong?
     (a) 47676; (b) D603; (c) 62006; (d) 34031; (e) 30027; (f) 2276; (g) 69617; (h) 44826; (i) 30903; (j) 4099; (k) 9435; (l) 90031; (m) 05564; (n) 45735; (o) D4; (p) 60803; (q) 30306; (r) 30582; (s) 61409.

107. How many standard BR steam locomotive designs are there?

108. What is the 'Midland Pullman'?

109. Which famous Pullman train is an electric multiple unit?

109. Which is the 'odd-man-out' among the following?
     Sturdee; *Conqueror*; *Defence*; *Warspite*; *Avenger*.

111. Which is the 'odd-man-out' among the following?
     Black Watch; *Royal Tank Corps*; *Royal Signals*; *Home Guard*.

112. Which is the 'odd-man-out' among the following?
     Prince Rupert; *Howard of Effingham*; *Robert Blake*; *Lord Howe*; *Lord Rodney*.

Rolling Stock (Answers on page 87)

113. What is a slip coach?

114. How many Royal coaches have been built to BR standard designs?

115. What is the diameter of a standard coach wheel?

116. What is the standard livery for BR main-line locomotive-hauled rolling stock?

117. What do the following codes mean?
     (a) RMB; (b) CK; (c) RSO; (d) GUV; (e) SK; (f) BSO; (g) RFO.

118. What is the chief purpose of the above codes?

119. What is the approximate weight of a standard coach?

120. What is the length of the BR standard main-line coach underframe?

121. What is a headstock?

122. What is the solebar?

123. In what year was the first BR standard coach completed?

124. How many seats has a standard first class compartment in a corridor vehicle?

125. The BR standard CK has four first class and three second class compartments with large windows. One of the second class windows can be unlocked and lifted up. Why?

126. A standard second class corridor coach for the LM, E/NE or ScR would have 48 seats, whereas if it had been built for the WR or SR it would have 64 seats. How is it possible to obtain 16 more seats on the latter regions' coaches?

127. Which type of gangway connection has the BR standard coach?

128. What is the seating capacity of a standard open first?

129. Is the buckeye type of coupling normally to be found on coaches with Pullman gangway connections?

130. Is a passenger carriage expected to last 20, 30, 40, 50 or 60 years?

131. When was the first corridor train with gangways throughout introduced in this country?

132. The diesel railcars used by BR are of two main types; one type is diesel-electric, but what is the other?

133. Which region favours the diesel-electric?

134. How many engines and of what horse power are used in a St Pancras/ Bedford four-car diesel set?

135. And what make are they?

136. What is the main difference between a three-car 'suburban' diesel and a three-car 'cross-country' diesel?

137. What is wrong with the following description of a coach? 'Driving trailer motor brake second'.

138. What is a multiple unit train set?

139. What is the overall width of a 'Hastings' six-car diesel set?

140. What form of transmission does it employ?

141. When were electrically hauled Pullman cars introduced on a British railway?

142. What is a 'Minfit'?

143. What is a 'Shocvan'?

144. What do the following coaching stock code letters denote?
    (a) semi-FO; (b) TBSO; (c) SS; (d) SCV; (e) BGZ; (f) SO(NG);
    (g) FL; (h) B; (i) SLC; (j) RSP; (k) RCAF.

145. On which region is standard coach number 9?

146. How many compartments have the following types of standard coach?
    (a) SK; (b) CK; (c) FK; (d) BSK; (e) BCK; (f) SLF.

147. How many double-deck electric coaches are there on the Southern Region?

148. How many Pullman coaches are allocated to the 'Brighton Belle' train?

149. What is a 'de-icer'?

150. What is (a) a 'Twin-Art'; (b) a 'Triple-art'; (c) a 'Quad-art'?

General knowledge and history (Answers on page 89)

151. Electricity for electric trains is received by overhead wires or a conductor rail. Say which method and voltage is used in each of the following areas?
    (a) SR Kent lines.
    (b) SR London/Portsmouth main line.
    (c) ER London /Southend Victoria.
    (d) NER Newcastle/Tyneside.
    (e) ScR. Glasgow Suburban.
    (f) LMR Lancaster/Morecambe/Heysham.
    (g) LMR Manchester/Bury.
    (h) LMR Manchester/Crewe.
    (i) LMR Liverpool/Southport.
    (j) LMR Manchester/Glossop.
    (k) LMR Manchester/Altrincham.
    (1) LMR Euston/Watford.
    (m) London Transport Railways.

152. Green is the standard livery for electric rolling stock. Are there any exceptions to this rule?

153. Southern electric trains have route indicators known as head codes.

There are, however, more routes than head codes. Name any two routes on which head code 08 will be found.

154. Which class of Type 4 main-line diesel locomotives has not received names?

155. When was third class accommodation renamed second class on BR?

156. Say what distance the following stations are from London by the normal direct route:

(a) Manchester; (b) Birmingham; (c) Stafford; (d) Holyhead; (e) Brighton; (f) Carlisle; (g) Doncaster; (h) Skegness; (i) Norwich; (j) Southend-on-Sea; (k) Ipswich; (l) Southampton; (m) Padstow (SR route); (n) Redhill; (o) Guildford; (p) Oxford; (q) Swindon; (r) Penzance; (s) Swansea; (t) Newcastle; (u) York; (v) Edinburgh; (w) Wick (via Carlisle and Perth); (x) Hull; (y) Cleethorpes; (z) Aberystwyth.

157. In the timetables the letters 'RB' and 'RC' appear. What do they mean?

158. How many different regional timetables are normally published each year?

159. Which region has tangerine as its regional colour?

160. Name 12 locomotive or carriage works (two from each region).

161. Are first class fares 100%, 50% or 25% above second class fares?

162. What are the special conditions by which circular tour tickets are issued?

163. Approximately how many steam locomotives were withdrawn between January 1955 and December 1958?

164. Is it an offence against the BTC Byelaws to use a portable radio on a train?

165. Is it an offence to smoke in a non-smoking compartment if the other passengers say that they do not mind?

166. In which year did the first mail train run?

167. In which year was the new Woodhead tunnel completed?

168. The BR emblem fixed to every locomotive and motor coach consists chiefly of a lion, and mounted on a crown and holding a railway

wheel. Should the lion face the front of the locomotive or train, or should it face left or right?

169. What famous train commenced service on 27 September 1935?

170. On what date did the 'Coronation Scot' first run?

171. Approximately how many staff are employed by British Railways?

172. What system of electrification has been adopted as the future standard on British Railways?

173. Which region is exempted from this decision and why?

174. Which were the first stretches of line to be electrified by the newly adopted system under the BR Modernisation Plan?

175. On which region are there no water troughs?

176. Mr John Ramsbottom, locomotive superintendent of the LNWR, laid down the first experimental water troughs. Where and when?

177. When was the Royal Albert Bridge, Saltash, opened?

178. And who designed it?

179. Where and when did the worst British railway bridge disaster occur?

180. When were the railways of Britain nationalised?

181. On which stretch of main line do trains from London and trains to London regulaly pass over the same track in the same direction?

182. Where are the highest water troughs in Great Britain situated?

183. Where are water troughs to be found inside a tunnel?

184. How long is the Forth Bridge?

185. How long is the Tay Bridge?

186. What is (a) a gravitational yard; (b) a hump yard?

187. What is a 'fitted' train?

188. What is the 'Condor'?

189. How many sleepers are used in one mile of track?

190. When was the ceremonial opening of the Stockton & Darlington Railway with George Stephenson's *Locomotion No 1*?

191. When was the first fatal railway accident, and which famous personality was involved?

192. In which years were the famous 'Railway races to the North' held?

193. When did the Southern Railway electrified services to Brighton and Worthing commence?

194. How many water troughs are there on the main line from King's Cross to Edinburgh, and which are nearest to King's Cross?

195. What is the longest stretch of track on British Railways without tunnels?

196. Which British main line has the most tunnels?

197. How many has it?

198. Which region has the longest British tunnel (excepting underground railways)?

199. How long is it?

200. Name the next three longest tunnels on BR.

201. Which region has the highest summit on British Railways?

202. How high is it, and where is it?

203. Which is the most mountainous British main line?

204. Which BR station has the most platforms?

205. Where is the longest British passenger station platform?

206. How long is it?

207. What is claimed to be the oldest locomotive in the world and where is it?

208. Where is the steepest gradient, worked by ordinary steam locomotives, in Britain?

209. Which British railway bridge has the longest span?

210. What is the length of the span?

211. Where was the world's first iron railway bridge?

212. Where is the longest straight track in Britain?

213. What do the following abbreviations stand for?
     (a) KESR; (b) LBSCR; (c) LYR; (d) GSWR; (e) CKPR;
     (f) GCR; (g) CLC; (h) LNWR; (i) MCR; (j) NBR; (k) GNR;
     (1) GNR(I); (m) WLER; (n) MSLR; (o) MSWJR; (p) HR;
     (q) HBR; (r) CR; (s) MR; (t) SECR; (u) LSWR; (v) NLR;

(w) EKR; (x) GER; (y) GWR; (z) FR.

214. What is commonly known as the 'Waverley' route?

215. When did the Great Western Railway complete the change over from broad to standard gauge?

216. What was the width between rails of Brunel's broad gauge?

217. When was the London-Birmingham railway opened throughout?

218. When was the London-Brighton line completed?

219. Which British railway tunnel took no less than 14 years to build?

220. What was the name given to the first locomotive to run on the GWR?

221. What was the first public railway with all traffic operated by steam?

222. When did it open?

223. What was the first public railway in London?

224. When were first class sleeping-cars in Great Britain first introduced and which railway company was responsible?

225. When were 'Pullman' cars introduced on the Midland Railway?

226. When was the 'Southern Belle' all-Pullman train introduced?

227. When were the 'Big Four' railway companies formed?

228. How many smaller companies were amalgamated?

229. What was the first main-line electrification in Britain with all traffic electrically hauled?

230. When were camping coaches introduced?

231. Electric locomotive No 26000 is named *Tommy*. Where and why did it receive this name?

232. When was the first section of the GWR from Paddington to Maidenhead opened?

233. When was the first electric railway in Britain opened?

234. Where was it?

235. When was the present Tay Bridge opened?

Track and Signalling (Answers on page 93)

236. What do the following signs denote?
 [see illustrations inside front cover]

237. On or near a signal post or gantry what do these signs denote?
 [see illustrations inside front cover]

238. What does this board alongside the track indicate?
 [see illustrations inside front cover]

239. What are the names given to these two types of rail?
 [see illustrations inside front cover]

240. Why is a slight gap left between the end of one length of rail and the next one?

241. What are the dimensions of a sleeper?

242. What is a check rail?

243. What is the purpose of the following: (a) chair; (b) sleeper; (c) key; (d) fishplate.

244. What is the principal advantage of the upper-quadrant type of signal?

245. Which pre-nationalisation railways adopted versions of automatic train control on certain lines?

246. What is the 'four foot'?

247. What is the width of the gap, or flangeway, between a check rail and the running rail?

248. What is the width between rails of the standard gauge used on British Railways?

249. What is a 'frog'?

250. What are facing points?

251. What are trailing points?

252. What is a fixed distant?

253. What are catch points?

254. What is a banner repeater signal?

255. What is a ground, or dwarf, frame?

256. What is a shunting disc?

257. What is a block section?

258. What are 'station limits'?

259. What is meant by absolute block working?

260. What colours does a distant signal show at night?

261. What are the indications shown by a four-aspect colour-light signal on British Railways?

262. What is the difference between a lower-quadrant and a somersault signal?

263. Which railways in the British Isles were noted for using the latter type?

264. What is 'CTC'?

265. What is a train staff and what is its use?

266. Name any two methods of working single lines.

267. What is interlocking?

268. What is a locking bar?

269. What is a trip arm?

Railway slang (Answers on page 96)

270. What are 'blinkers'?

271. What is a 'peg' or 'board'?

272. What is meant by train crews 'going home on the cushions'?

273. What is a 'dummy'?

274. What is an 'auto' or 'motor'?

275. What is a 'blower'?

Answers

Locomotives

A1. A Compound locomotive is one in which steam is expanded in two stages, from high-pressure to low-pressure cylinders, thus preventing the cylinders from suffering the extreme changes of temperature created by the process of expansion. The most familiar Compound locomotives in Britain are the Midland and LMS 4-4-0 class, of which No 41000 has been restored to 1914 condition, as MR 1000, at Derby Works.

A2. One in which the steam passes through a series of elements, drying it and making it hotter. In a non-superheated engine the steam passes into the cylinders in a 'wet' or what is called a 'saturated' condition.

A3. GWR No 111 *The Great Bear* built at Swindon in 1908 and later rebuilt as a 4-6-0 of the 'Castle' class.

A4. The last BR 'Pacific' design to appear was 71000 *Duke of Gloucester* built at Crewe in 1954.

A5. It has three cylinders and Caprotti valve gear.

A6. No 1000 *County of Middlesex* was built with a double chimney.

A7. A chain drive enclosed in an oil bath.

A8. No 35018 *British India Line*, 1956.

A9. 0-10-0.

A10. 'Big Bertha'.

A11. 58100.

A12. A canopy, or baffle, of firebrick laid across the firebox tubeplate to delay the escape of the hot gases and ensure proper combustion before they are drawn through the boiler tubes.

A13. An extension, downwards inside the smokebox, of the chimney of a locomotive.

A14. To reduce the emission of smoke and steam whilst working through long tunnels or underground railways.

A15. In a diesel-electric locomotive the diesel engine drives an electricity generator which in turn feeds orthodox traction motors. In a diesel-hydraulic locomotive the diesel engine itself (or engines) is used to move the locomotive, by the use of hydraulic transmission and torque converters, thereby dispensing with the diesel-electric's added and complicated electrical equipment.

A16. The Western Region.

A17. 'Priming' is the condition of a loco when water from the boiler passes, unevaporated, with the steam into the cylinders, and ultimately out via the chimney – showering nearby objects.

A18. (a) Two, (b) Four, (c) Four, (d) Two, (e) Three, (f) Three, (g) Four, (h) Three.

A19. Sir Nigel Gresley. 1935.

A20. It was an experimental high-pressure four-cylinder compound with water-tube boiler.

A21. 60700, 1959.

A22. (a) 'Atlantic', (b) 'Mogul', (c) 'Pacific'.

A23. So called because it was invented by a Belgian engineer, Egide Walschaerts (1820-1901), in 1844.

A24. The propulsive force exerted by the driving wheel at its point of contact with the rail.

A25. The end of the connecting rod which bears on the crank pin.

A26. The Southern Region 'Schools' class. Designed by R. E. L. Maunsell in 1930; some modified by O. V. S. Bulleid from 1938 onwards with multiple-jet blastpipe. TE 25,135lb.

A27. One of the cylindrical sections from which the boiler barrel is built up.

A28. The London, Midland & Scottish Railway. No 6202. Later BR 46202. After rebuilding as an orthodox four-cylinder locomotive and named *Princess Anne* it was involved in the disastrous collision at Harrow & Wealdstone on 8 October 1952 and subsequently scrapped.

A29. *City of London* and *East Anglian* were specially streamlined for working the 'East Anglian' express.

A30. It is the British Railways power classification denoting the suitability of each engine for a particular duty. The letter 'P' indicates a class primarily suited to passenger work and 'F' for freight work. When both letters are included or the letters 'MT' (Mixed Traffic) used the class is suited to passenger and freight duty. The lowest is classed as '0' and the highest '8' for passenger or '9' for freight.

A31. It denotes the route availability of each type of locomotive.

A32. WR locomotives carry a painted colour circle on the cab sides; the colour of the circle denotes the routes over which the locomotive may work.

A33. The first main-line diesel-electric locomotive to run on a British railway was LMS No 10000, built at Derby Works in 1947.

A34. 2000hp 2-D-2 (4-8-4) No 10100, the most powerful diesel-mechanical locomotive in the world. Introduced 1951, Derby Works, LMR. Withdrawn 1959. The transmission was based on the design by Col Fell.

A35. The Great Eastern Railway 0-10-0 tank locomotive called the 'Decapod'.

A36. Vertical poppet type cylinder valves operated by a camshaft driving off the main wheels of the locomotive.

A37. No 71000 *Duke of Gloucester* and Standard Class 5 4-6-0s Nos. 73125-73154.

A38. (a) 35,455lb or 33,616lb, (b) 40,000lb, (c) 25,320lb, (d) 26,610lb, (e) 37,400lb, (f) 31,625lb, (g) 27,520lb, (h) 27,275lb.

A39. None.

A40. A revolutionary 0-6-6-0T, designed by O. V. S. Bulleid for the SR, which did not pass the experimental stage.

A41. Valves below the cylinders to permit the escape of water trapped inside them.

A42. A device fitted in the crown of the inner firebox, comprising a plug of soft metal which melts and releases steam into the firebox if the water on top should run dry. An anti-explosion device.

A43. (a) 2300/2500hp, (b) 1000hp, (c) 1000/1100hp, (d) 2,200hp, (e) 1160hp, (f) 2000hp, (g) 800hp.

A44. D8000, June 1957.

A45. 3,300hp. Named after the Napier 'Deltic' engines which power it.

The cylinders are arranged in the form of an inverted triangle, hence the name 'Deltic'.

A46. By code letters and figures on an oval-shaped plate affixed to the lower half of the smokebox door.

A47. A raised ridge around the forward part of the chimney ring, to screen the chimney mouth from air currents that would otherwise beat the discharging exhaust backwards.

A48. An experimental 25kV ac electric locomotive for trials and crew training on the LMR Manchester-Crewe line. Numbered E1000 and later renumbered E2001.

A49. (a) 1Co-Co1, (b) 1Co-Co1, (c) Co-Co, (d) A1A-A1A, (e) B-B, (f) 0-6-0, (g) 0-4-0, (h) 0-6-0, (i) Co-Bo, (j) Bo-Bo, (k) Bo-Bo, (l) B-B. (m) Bo-Bo, (n) Co-Co, (o) Bo-Bo.

A50. (a) Stockton & Darlington Railway, (b) GWR, (c) FR, (d) LNWR, (e) GNSR, (f) LBSCR, (g) HR, (h) GNR, (i) GWR, (j) LBSCR.

A51. They are all historical locomotives preserved by the British Transport Commission.

A52. A taper boiler is intended to provide more steam space nearest the firebox, where steam is most liberally generated, as on ex-GWR and some LMS locomotives.

A53. The U-shaped member in which the axle box slides up and down as the wheel traverses irregularities in the track.

A54. 83 tons.

A55. The LNER and the LMSR.

A56. The SR Bulleid Pacifics as originally built.

A57. (a) LMR Stanier Class 5 4-6-0, (b) SR Bulleid Pacifics or SR Class Q1 0-6-0, (c) LMR '3F' standard 0-6-0T, (d) SR 'T9' 4-4-0, (e) SR 'A1X' 0-6-0T,. (f) WR 90XX 4-4-0, (g) LMR Ivatt '2' 2-6-0.

A58. The Southern Region.

A59. A locomotive travelling by itself without a train attached.

A60. A solid mass added to the inner rim of a locomotive driving wheel, placed in such a way as to compensate for the loss of equilibrium induced by various moving parts of the engine.

A61. 2,552hp.

A62. Doncaster Works, ER.

A63. The 'Night Ferry' from Victoria to Dover.

A64. A locomotive used by the railway for its own services (usually for the use of the various engineers departments), and not employed in normal revenue-earning service.

A65. An iron arm projecting downwards in front of a locomotive's or railcar's leading wheels for the purpose of removing small objects from its path, to avert the possibility of derailment.

A66. The housing containing the steam distribution valve.

A67. Six and four respectively.

A68. To divert the flow of air passing along a locomotive in an upward direction, to force the exhaust from the chimney clear of the driver's line of vision.

A69. It contains the axle-bearings (plain or roller bearings) and transmits the weight of the locomotive onto the axle.

A70. It has become overheated due to lack of lubrication, and the bearings may become molten and fused together.

A71. The brackets affixed to a locomotive on which the oil-lamps are placed.

A72. A large casting that supports the smokebox and boiler front end.

A73. A pony truck carries a leading non-driving axle, the whole assembly being allowed side play under the control of a pivoted radius bar. Its purpose is to lead an engine smoothly into a curve.

A74. A radial truck serves a similar purpose to a pony truck but the axle boxes themselves are allowed side play within the main frames of the locomotive.

A75. No 92165/6/7.

A76. Ventilators to allow air to escape when the tender or side tank is being filled with water.

A77. WR 'Castle', 13ft 5½in.

A78. 7 coaches, between Corby and Essendine, descending Stoke bank on the East Coast main line; 126mph, 3 July 1938.

A79. A type used extensively in modern practice, in which the crown of the firebox shell is made flat. So called after its inventor Alfred Belpaire (1820-1893).

A80. The ashpan is beneath the firebox, to catch ash raked out of the firebox.

A81. (d) The SR 'West Country' has three cylinders and is a 4-6-2, the others are two-cylinder 4-6-0s.

A82. They are all 'mixed-traffic' designs.

A83. The 'Coronation' class has four cylinders, the others three.

A84. (a) 1927, Collett, (b) 1935, Gresley, (c) 1927, Gresley, (d) 1943, Stanier, (e) 1941, Bulleid, (f) 1933, Stanier, (g) 1934, Stanier, (h) 1923, Collett, (i) 1945, Bulleid, (j) 1936, Gresley, (k) 1926, Maunsell.

A85. A steam locomotive when 'cold', ie, no steam has been raised inside the boiler.

A86. An assisting engine in front of the train engine. A 'station pilot' an engine engaged in station duties and acting as a standby in case of emergency. Years ago there was a Royal Train pilot, a special engine running in advance of the Royal Train.

A87. 114mph near Crewe by 4-6-2. 6220 *Coronation* (now 46220) on 29 June 1937.

A88. SR 'Q1' 0-6-0, introduced 1942.

A89. O. V. S. Bulleid, 30,080lb.

A90. E3001, November 1959.

Spotters' Corner

A91. 30863, 'Lord Nelson' class.

A92. 45643, 'Jubilee' class.

A93. 'Patriot' class.

A94. (a) 22,515lb, (b) 19,755lb, (c) 20,835lb, (d) 23,635lb.

A95. (a) E*nterprise*, (b) *Princess Victoria*, (c) *The Green Howards*, (d) *Howard of Effingham*, (e) *Bude*, (f) *Mayflower,* (g) *King Richard III.* (h) *Champion*, (i) *City of Stoke on Trent*, (i) *Skiddaw*, (k) *Tommy*, (1) *Bulldog*, (m) *Merlin.* (n) *Abney Hall,* (o) *Alfred the Great*,

(p) *Royal Scots Grey*, (q) *Green Arrow*, (r) *Great Western*, (s) *Royal Mail*, (t) *Sir Eustace Missenden, Southern Railway*, (u) *Clan Stewart*, (v) *Private W. Wood V.C.,* (w) *King's Wimbledon*, (x) *Windsor Castle*, (y) *A. H. Peppercorn*, (z) *Great Eastern*.

A96. ER Class A4.

A97. 7P.

A98. 842.

A99. 45154 *Lanarkshire Yeomanry*, 45156 *Ayrshire Yeomanry*, 45157 The *Glasgow Highlander*, 45158 *Glasgow Yeomanry*.

A100. E. Thompson.

A101. Derby.

A102. Crewe.

A103. 12.

A104. (a) Camden, (b) St. Margarets (Edinburgh), (c) Derby, (d) Wolverhampton (Stafford Rd), (e) Bournemouth Central, (f) Oswestry, (g) Shoeburyness, (h) Ipswich, (i) Newton Heath, (j) Darlington, (k) Hornsey, (l) Longsight, (m) Inverness, (n) Brighton, (o) Swindon, (p) Polmadie (Glasgow).

A105. 1D, Devons Road (Bow), London.

A106. (a) LMR 3F 0-6-0T, (b) North British Locomotive Co Type 4 'Warship' class 2,000hp diesel-hydraulic A1A-A1A, (c) ER 'K1', (d) SR 'West Country', (e) SR 'M7', (f) W.R. '2251', (g) ER 'N7', (h) LMR Class 5, (i) SR 'Schools', (j) WR 'Castle', (k) WR '94XX', (l) WD 'Austerity' 2-8-0, (m) 'Brush' Traction Type 2 1,365hp. diesel-electric A1A-A1A, (n) LMR 'Jubilee', (o) Derby/Sulzer Type 4 2,300hp 'Peak' Class 1 Co-Co1, (p) ER 'V2', (q) SR '700', (r) SR '0415', (s) ER 'B1'.

A107. 12.

A108. A six-car 'de-luxe' diesel-electric, all-first class Pullman train for service on the Midland Division of the LMR

A109. The 'Brighton Belle'.

A110. *Avenger* is a 'Warship' class diesel, the others are all 'Jubilee' 4-6-0s.

A111. *Black Watch* is a 'Royal Scot'; the others are all 'Patriot' class locomotives.

A112. *Prince Rupert* is a 'Jubilee' class locomotive, the others are all 'Lord Nelson' class. *Howard of Effingham* is in both classes – Nos 45670 and 30854 both carry the name.

Rolling stock

A113. A slip coach can be uncoupled from the remainder of the train while travelling at speed. It has to be at the rear of the train. The Guard works the slip apparatus and controls the vehicle, when isolated from the remainder of the train, by means of the brake.

A114. Three coaches.

A115. 3ft 6in.

A116. Maroon with black and gold lining.

A117. (a) Open second with miniature buffet, (b) Corridor composite, (c) Restaurant open second, d) General Utility Van, (e) Second corridor, (f) Brake second open, (g) Restaurant open first.

A118. They are telegraphic codes.

A119. 32-35 tons.

A120. 63ft 5in.

A121. The headstock is the part of the underframe on to which the buffers and drawgear are fixed.

A122. The solebar is a longitudinal girder connecting the two headstocks.

A123. 1950.

A124. Six in all, three-a-side.

A125. To admit stretchers.

A126. The SR and WR coaches do not have arm-rests and reserve four seats each side. LMR, E/NE and ScR stock has arm-rests and reserve three-a-side. During busy periods passengers are expected to put the arm-rests up and sit four-a-side.

A127. Pullman gangway connections.

A128. 42 seats.

A129. Yes.

A130. 30 years.

A131. 1891 by the Great Western Railway.

A132. Diesel-mechanical.

A133. Southern Region.

A134. Four 238hp

A135. Rolls-Royce.

A136. A three-car 'suburban' diesel has doors to each bay and no gangway connections. The 'cross-country' type is gangwayed and has fewer doors per coach.

A137. It must either be driving 'trailer' brake second or driving 'motor' brake second; it cannot, of course, be both.

A138. A train set incorporating its own power unit or units capable of being coupled to similar sets and driven by one man in the leading unit.

A139. 8ft 2½in.

A140. Electric transmission.

A141. 1 June 1910 by the Metropolitan Railway.

A142. A mineral wagon fitted with the vacuum brake.

A143. A van equipped with shock absorbers to minimise damage to merchandise due to violent shunting, etc.

A144. (a) A semi-open first class coach, (b) Tourist brake second open, (c) Saloon second, (d) Special cattle vehicle, (e) Six-wheeled brake van (gangwayed), (f) Second open (non gangwayed), (g) First (lavatory) non gangwayed, (h) Bogie brake van. (i) Composite sleeping car, (j) Pantry second, (k) Cafeteria.

A145. Southern Region.

A146. (a) eight, (b) four 1st, three 2nd, (c) seven, (d) four, (e) two 1st, three 2nd, (f) eleven 1st, attendant one.

A147. Eight, formed into two four-car units.

A148. 15 (three five-car units).

A149. A special vehicle usually marshalled into an electric train in frosty weather to spray the conductor rails with de-icing fluid.

A150. (a) A two-coach articulated set, (b) A three-coach articulated set, (c) A four-coach articulated set.

General knowledge and history

A151. (a) Third rail, 750 volts dc, (b) Third rail, 750 volts dc, (c) Overhead, 1,500 volts dc, (d) Third rail, 630 volts dc, (e) Overhead, 25,000 volts ac, (f) Overhead, 6,600 volts ac, (g) Protected side contact third rail, 1,200 volts dc, (h) Overhead, 25,000 volts ac, (i) Third rail, 630 volts dc, (j) Overhead, 1,500 volts dc, (k) Overhead, 1,500 volts dc, (1 & m) Third and fourth rail 630 volts dc.

A152. Yes. LTE Red, ScR. Glasgow suburban, 'Caledonian Blue'.

A153. Any of the following: — Waterloo-Portsmouth Harbour; Victoria-Sutton; Victoria-East Croydon; Charing Cross-Gillingham.

A154. D200 class.

A155. 3 June 1956.

A156. (a) 194 miles, (b) 113 miles, (c) 133 miles, (d) 264 miles, (e) 50 miles, (f) 299 miles, (g) 156 miles, (h) 131 miles, (i) 115 miles, (j) 36 miles, (k) 69 miles. (1) 79 miles, (m) 260 miles, (n) 20/23 miles, (o) 30 miles, (p) 63 miles, (q) 77 miles, (r) 325 miles, (s) 191 miles, (t) 268 miles, (u) 188 miles, (v) 393 miles, (w) 729 miles, (x) 205 miles, (y) 104 miles, (z) 277 miles.

A157. 'RB' means that a buffet car is provided, 'RC' means that a restaurant car is provided.

A158. Twelve (one for each region twice a year).

A159. North Eastern Region.

A160. Two of: — Inverurie, St. Rollox or Cowlairs (Scottish).
Two of: — Swindon, Wolverhampton, or Caerphilly (Western).
Two of: — York, Darlington, or Faverdale (North Eastern).
Two of: — Eastleigh, Lancing or Ashford (Southern).
Stratford and Doncaster (Eastern).
Two of: — Wolverton, Derby, Gorton, Crewe or Horwich (London Midland).

A161. 50%.

A162. Three or more consecutive point-to-point journeys in Great Britain and Ireland commencing and terminating in the same town, which cannot be covered by a through booking or ordinary return fares. A reduction of about 10% on the single fare is allowed, with a minimum fare of 23/- second class.

A163. 2,800.

A164. It is if other passengers show annoyance.

A165. It is an offence to smoke in a non-smoking compartment even with the conditions mentioned in the question.

A166. 1840.

A167. 1953.

A16S. The lion should be facing left.

A169. The 'Silver Jubilee'.

A170. 5 July1937.

A171. 550,000.

A172. High voltage 50-cycle ac system.

A173. The Southern Region, as it is already committed to the 750 volts dc third rail system.

A174. The first trial stretch of the Manchester-Crewe line and the Colchester to Clacton and Walton line.

A175. The Southern Region.

A176. 1859, between Llanfairfechan and Aber, LNWR.

A177. May 1859.

A178. Isambard Kingdom Brunel.

A179. The Tay Bridge disaster, 28 December 1879.

A180. 1 January 1948.

A181. From Exeter (St Davids) to Cowley Bridge Junction and from Devonport Junction to Plymouth (North Road).

A182. Garsdale (Hawes) troughs are the highest in Great Britain, over 1,100ft above sea level.

A183. Diggle troughs, inside Standedge tunnel.

A184. 1 mile 46 chains.

A185. 2 miles 16½ chains.

A186. (a) A marshalling yard constructed on a long falling gradient so that wagons will run by gravity from siding to siding; (b) A marshalling yard with an artificially made hump, so that wagons, having been pushed to the top of the hump by a locomotive, will run down under their own momentum into the sorting sidings.

A187. A train fitted with the vacuum brake throughout.

A188. A name applied to a diesel-hauled express fitted freight train composed of road-rail containers on flat wagons, giving door-to-door service. The first train of this type runs from Hendon to Gushetfaulds near Glasgow.

A189. 2,112.

A190. 27 September 1825.

A191. 15 September 1830, at the opening of Liverpool & Manchester Railway. Mr. Huskisson MP was run over and killed.

A192. 1888 London to Edinburgh, 1895 London to Aberdeen.

A193. 1 January 1933.

A194. Six. Langley (26½ miles) is the nearest to King's Cross.

A195. 223½ miles. From Preston Brook Tunnel (177 miles from Euston) to Eglinton St. Tunnel, Glasgow.

A196. St. Pancras-Carlisle, 308.1 miles.

A197. 22.

A198. Western Region. Severn Tunnel.

A199. 4 miles 628yd.

A200. (a) Totley, between Dore & Totley and Grindlesford, 3 miles 950yd. (b) Standedge, Yorks. (Liverpool-Leeds route), 3 miles 60yd. (c) Woodhead, 3 miles 13yd.

A201. The Scottish Region.

A202. Druimuachdar (Drumochter), between Dalnaspidal and Dalwhinnie, 1,484ft above sea-level.

A203. Perth-Inverness, ScR.

A204. Waterloo. 21 main line and two Waterloo & City underground. Total 23.

A205. Manchester, Victoria and Exchange, LMR.

A206. 2,194ft.

A207. *Puffing Billy*, Science Museum, Kensington, built 1813 by William Hedley at Wylam Colliery.

A208. Hopton incline, Cromford & High Peak line LMR 1 in 14.

A209. The Forth Bridge, ScR.

A210. 1,710ft.

A211. Over the River Gaunless, 1823, designed by George Stephenson.

A212. Selby and Hull, NER, 18 miles.

A213. (a) Kent & East Sussex Railway, (b) London, Brighton & South Coast Railway, (c) Lancashire & Yorkshire Railway, (d) Glasgow & South Western Railway, (e) Cockermouth, Keswick & Penrith Railway, (f) Great Central Railway, (g) Cheshire Lines Committee, (h) London & North Western Railway, (i) Maryport & Carlisle Railway, (j) North British Railway, (k) Great Northern Railway. (l) Great Northern Railway (Ireland), (m) West London Extension Railway, (n) Manchester, Sheffield & Lincolnshire Railway, (o) Midland & South Western Junction Railway, (p) Highland Railway, (q) Hull & Barnsley Railway, (r) Caledonian Railway, (s) Midland Railway, (t) South Eastern & Chatham Railway, (u) London & South Western Railway, (v) North London Railway, (w) East Kent Railway, (x) Great Eastern Railway, (y) Great Western Railway, (z) Furness Railway.

A214. Carlisle-Edinburgh (Waverley).

A215. 23 May 1892.

A216. 7ft 0¼in.

A217. 17 September 1838.

A218. 1841

A219. The Severn Tunnel.

A220. *Vulcan.*

A221. The Liverpool & Manchester Railway.

A222. 15 September 1830.

A223. The London & Greenwich Railway, 8 February 1836.

A224. 31 July 1873. East Coast Scottish expresses, by North British Railway.

A225. 1 June 1874.

A226. 1908, London and Brighton, LBSCR.

A227. 1 January 1923.

A228. 123.

A229. The Manchester-Sheffield-Wath scheme of the LNER completed by the ER in 1954.

A230. 1933.

A231. It was named after the familiar nickname of British soldiers by the people of the Netherlands after the locomotive had run trials in Holland, soon after the 1939-45 War.

A232. 4 June 1838.

A233. 1883.

A234. Volks electric railway along Brighton beach.

A235. 13 June 1887

Track and signalling

A236. (A1) Advanced warning board indicating a temporary speed restriction with permitted speed (in this case 5mph), (A2) Commencement of temporary speed restriction, (A3) Termination of temporary speed restriction, (A4) Permanent speed limit (in this case 70mph).

A237. (B1) Telephone or plunger nearby to communicate with signal box, (B2) The line is track circuited, (B3) Telephone box.

A238. Beginning of water troughs.

A239. (a) Flat bottom rail, (b) Bullhead rail.

A240. To allow for expansion of the metal, caused by changing temperatures.

A241. 8ft 6in x 10in x 5in

A242. An additional rail set inside, and close to, the inner running rail of a curve for the purpose of aiding the passage of the wheels and to prevent a tendency to derail.

A243. (a) To carry the rail and join it to the sleeper, (b) To support the rails and maintain the stability of the track, (c) A wedge between rail and chair to hold the rail firm, (d) To join one length of rail to the next.

A244. In the event of a failure, such as a broken wire, the arm returns to the danger or stop position without the need for cumbersome balance weights.

A245. The London, Tilbury & Southend line of the LMSR, and the Great Western Railway.

A246. The space between the two rails of standard gauge track.

A247. 1¾in.

A248. 4ft 8½in.

A249. On points and crossings it is a piece of rail built to 'Vee' shape at the actual intersection of the two tracks.

A250. Points splitting the line into two diverging tracks in the direction of travel.

A251. Points joining two converging lines in the direction of travel.

A252. A distant signal permanently fixed at 'caution'.

A253. Automatic points held open by a spring so that any vehicle entering them from the facing direction will be derailed. They are normally placed in a trailing direction on lines having steep gradients to derail any runaway vehicles in the wrong direction.

A254. A repeater signal in the form of a black rectangular arm contained in a circular glass-fronted casing.

A255. A small cluster of point and signal levers released by a distant box, but manipulated on the spot. There is generally no complicated interlocking and the frame is at ground level.

A256. A small signal, generally at ground level, in the form of a white circular disc, with a red or yellow stripe painted on it.

A257. The section of line from the last stop signal controlled by one signal box to the first stop signal controlled by the signal box ahead.

A258. The section of line from the first to the last stop signal controlled by one signal box.

A259. The system under which only one train can be in a block section on one line at one time. This is the normal method of working passenger lines.

A260. A yellow light for caution, or green for clear.

A261. Red — Stop. Yellow — Caution. Double Yellow — Preliminary Caution. Green — Clear.

A262. A lower-quadrant signal has the arm and spectacle casting joined as one piece, pivoted near the right-hand end. A somersault signal has the arm and spectacle as separate parts; the arm is pivoted in the centre and in the clear position is almost vertical.

A263. Great Northern Railway, The Midland & Great Northern Railway, Belfast & County Down Railway, and some South Wales railways.

A264. Centralised Traffic Control. A system by which one signalman can control many miles of line from switches on a diagram of the track layout, the equipment operating points and signals by electronic impulses. In the United States some CTC installations control more than 100 miles of track from one centre.

A265. A wood or metal 'stick' given to the driver of a train on a single line as his authority to be on the single line. The staff is engraved with the names of the stations between which it applies. Also serving the same purpose are 'key tokens', 'miniature staffs' or 'tablets'. There is only one staff for any one single line section, or if an electric token or tablet is used, only one can be taken out of the instruments at one time.

A266. One-engine-in-steam-staff; Staff and ticket; Electric token, tablet or miniature staff; Pilotman (human 'staff' used during engineering works on double lines, or if the token instruments are damaged).

A267. Electrical or mechanical locking on a lever frame to prevent signals and/or points giving conflicting indications.

A268. A bar connected to a facing point lock and held down by the wheels of passing trains to prevent the lock being withdrawn and the points changed under a train.

A269. A device on the line near a signal which, when the signal is at danger, will engage with apparatus on the train to stop it should the train run past. It is used on all London Transport lines and on certain British Railways local electric lines.

Railway slang

A270. Smoke deflectors.

A271. A signal arm.

A272. Returning home as a passenger in the train.

A273. A small shunting signal at the track side.

A274. A 'push and pull' train.

A275. In the slang sense a telephone, also a locomotive part.